Energy Savings with Home Improvements

Energy Savings with
Home Improvements

Practical advice based on the Energy
Efficiency Office's MONERGY campaign
which can benefit all homeowners

Published by
Consumers' Association
and Hodder & Stoughton

Energy Savings with Home Improvements is published by
Consumers' Association, 14 Buckingham Street, London
WC2N 6DS and Hodder & Stoughton Limited, 47 Bedford
Square, London WC1B 3DP

British Library Cataloguing in Publication Data

Energy savings with home improvements: practical advice
  based on the Department of Energy's MONERGY
  campaign which can benefit all homeowners.
  1. Dwellings—Great Britain—Energy conversation—
  Amateurs' manuals
  I. Consumers' Association
  644   TJ163.5.D86

ISBN 0 340 39980 5

This guide has been written and illustrated for the Energy
Efficiency Office of the Department of Energy by NBA
Tectonics under the direction of the Building Research
Energy Conservation Support Unit (BRECSU) and with
advice from the Government's Building Research
Establishment (BRE).

Cover illustration by Michael Terry
Design and typography by DP Press, St Julians,
Sevenoaks, Kent
Printed and bound in Great Britain by
Hazell Watson & Viney Ltd
Member of the BPCC Group
Aylesbury, Bucks.

CONTENTS

FOREWORD
by the Secretary of State for Energy, the Rt Hon Peter Walker, MBE, MP

I am delighted that Consumers' Association has collaborated with my Energy Efficiency Office to produce this guide to energy saving in the home. It is all the more appropriate that the guide is being published for the first time in Energy Efficiency Year. Written under the direction of the Building Research Energy Conservation Support Unit, it describes how you can improve the energy efficiency of your home at minimum cost to you and with minimum disruption – helping to make it more comfortable and cheaper to run.

It does this by emphasising the value of installing energy efficiency measures when you are carrying out other improvement work – indeed, in many cases the cost of the additional work is minimal. In a helpful and practical way, the guide takes you through every area of your home and describes all the energy efficiency opportunities open to you.

Detailed information with illustrations on the measures you can take is given in the Topic Sheets. Many of the measures they describe are well within the scope of DIY home improvers; others may require a builder or a specialist – the Topic Sheet always makes this clear.

Home improvements are a golden opportunity to get the most from the money you spend on energy. This comprehensive guide tells you everything you need to know. I am sure that you will read and use it with interest.

PETER WALKER

WHO THE GUIDE IS FOR

If you are about to improve your home this guide is for you. It tells you about the energy saving measures which you should consider incorporating into your modernisation plans both to improve your comfort and to reduce future heating bills.

The ideal time to improve the energy efficiency of your home is when major improvements are being undertaken. The additional work is likely to cause the minimum of disruption and the extra cost will probably be small compared to other improvements, especially if done at the same time.

The guide will help if you are:

- improving your home with an improvement or repair grant
- extending your house
- modernising your home bit by bit as money becomes available
- doing the work yourself
- getting a builder to do the work.

It covers the following topics:

- insulation of floors, walls and roofs
- reducing heat lost through windows and doors
- reducing draughts and providing controllable ventilation
- selecting an efficient, well-controlled heating and hot water system.

FINDING YOUR WAY AROUND THE GUIDE

Summary

For a quick guide to energy saving measures and likely costs look opposite and overleaf.

Where does the heat go?

To help you understand where heat is lost and how to make your home warmer and more comfortable, turn to page 11.

Where can I save energy?

The tables on pages 16–35 set out the range of energy saving improvements for each part of your home.

How do I go about it?

Thirteen Topic Sheets from page 38 onwards describe how to do the work yourself or what points to consider if you need to call in a specialist. If you are employing a builder you can use the Topic Sheets to show him how you want the work carried out.

What does that term mean?

The glossary on page 109 contains building terms used in the guide which you may not find in a standard dictionary.

1 **Pitched roof** Where loft insulation is being added, OPPORTUNITY to seal gaps and cracks in the ceiling before adding insulation, increase the thickness of insulation and ensure adequate ventilation

2 **Heating system** When a complete new heating system is to be installed, OPPORTUNITY to select a modern, efficient boiler which is matched to the better insulation of the house, together with effective temperature controls

3 **Windows** Where an existing window frame is replaced or a new window formed, OPPORTUNITY to install new window with built-in draught proofing, double glazing and trickle ventilation

4 **Flat roof** If there is a poor leaking roof finish or a defective ceiling, OPPORTUNITY to add insulation as part of the repair work

5 **Walls – solid** Where internal plaster is removed as part of damp proofing treatment or demolition work, OPPORTUNITY to add insulation behind the new wall finish

6 **New extension** If you are building a new extension, OPPORTUNITY to include a high level of insulation and draughtproofing

7 **Walls – solid** Where render is old and cracked, or brickwork or other finish is in poor condition, OPPORTUNITY to add external wall insulation system, to include new render or cladding

ENERGY SAVING OPPORTUNITIES — A QUICK GUIDE

Homes undergoing renovation and improvement work offer the ideal opportunity to bring them up to a standard comparable to the best modern houses by upgrading insulation, controlling ventilation and installing an efficient, well-controlled heating and hot water system.

It is easier, as well as cheaper, to include many energy saving measures during modernisation, rather than add them at a later date.

For example, if your modernisation involves laying a new concrete floor, it is an easy job to incorporate insulation during construction, but to insulate the floor at a later date would cause considerable disruption. So you should seriously consider the opportunities (see pages 16–35) offered by your proposed building works – it could save you money on future heating bills and make your house more comfortable.

When considering ideas from the guide, it is important to be aware that combining several measures into an energy efficient package often provides additional opportunities and savings. For example, insulating your house will save money on the cost of a new heating installation. This is because the better insulated the house the less heat it loses, and the smaller the radiators and boiler need be to keep you warm. So list *all* the energy saving opportunities for your house and consider the implications of combining several improvements.

8 Floors – suspended timber When floorboards are taken up to lay new water, gas or electrical services, or where timber rot is suspected, OPPORTUNITY to add insulation before replacing the floorboards

9 Floors – solid Where the screed is cracking or suffering from rising damp, and the floor has to be replaced, OPPORTUNITY to add insulation under the new floor finish

10 Kitchen and bathroom When fittings are to be replaced, OPPORTUNITY to insulate the inside of solid walls before the new fittings are installed

11 Walls – cavity Where walls are in a suitable condition, OPPORTUNITY to add cavity wall insulation

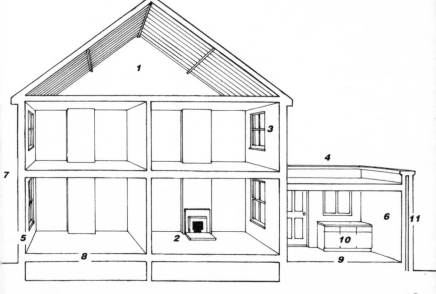

Rateable values and energy savings

Large-scale home improvements will affect the rateable value of your house. However, none of the following items is counted as contributing to the rateable value and will not therefore increase your rates:

- insulation
- draughtproofing
- double glazing
- heating controls.

Even adding central heating will not increase your rates until the next national reassessment of rateable values, provided you are not dividing your house into separate units.

Comparison of installation costs

(For a typical semi-detached house)

Measures costing under £25 each

- Insulate hot water cylinder
- Draughtproof and insulate the trap door into the loft
- Add reflective foil behind radiators
- Seal gaps around pipes and cables passing through walls, floors and ceilings
- Add DIY draughtproofing and a new threshold to external doors.

£25–£50

- Add DIY draughtproofing to windows
- On a new concrete floor use insulation and chipboard as the finished floor instead of normal sand/cement screed
- Builder to draughtproof and add new threshold to an external door
- Add extra insulation to 10m² flat roof.

£50–£150

- Add thermostatic radiator valves (about £10 extra for each radiator)
- Add extract fan to kitchen or bathroom
- DIY 100 mm loft insulation
- DIY insulation to timber ground floor (where there is access from below)
- DIY – lay hardboard over suspended timber ground floor and draughtproof
- Builder to draughtproof windows.

£150–£300

- Extra cost of replacing new external timber door with energy efficient door, frame and draughtproofing.
- Add thermostats and diverter valve to heating system
- Builder to insulate loft to 100 mm
- Builder to insulate timber ground floor (where there is access from below)
- Add a new door and frame across the hallway to form a draught lobby

- Simple DIY secondary double glazing to all windows
- Add insulation below new concrete ground floor
- Builder to lay hardboard over suspended timber ground floor and draughtproof
- Cavity wall insulation (for small terraced house).

£300–£600

- Cavity wall insulation
- Builder to insulate timber ground floor from above
- Extra cost of double glazing and draughtproofing replacement windows.

over £600

- DIY internal wall insulation
- Professional secondary double glazing
- Install central heating
- Builder to insulate walls internally
- Replacement double glazed windows
- External wall insulation.

(Arranged in order of increasing costs and based on 1986 prices.)

HEAT AND YOUR HOME

We use energy to provide space heating to keep us warm and comfortable according to weather conditions and to provide hot water.

The heating system only provides part of that energy. Several other sources of energy warm the house:

- all the electricity used for lighting and appliances such as irons, kettles, hair driers and televisions ending up as heat
- the heat from our bodies
- the energy used for cooking
- the sunlight that shines through the windows warming up the walls, floor and furniture.

The relative contributions of the heating system and the gains from these other sources vary through the year: for instance, the heating system provides little or nothing in the summer but gives by far the largest contribution on a cold day in winter. Eliminating unnecessary heat losses reduces the heating required from the heating system in cold weather, and increases the length of time in spring and autumn when no extra heating is required.

Once a steady indoor temperature has been achieved (more correctly, a steady temperature difference between inside and outside), the rate of heat flowing in (from all sources) exactly balances the rate of heat flowing out. The rate of heat loss depends on:

- the resistance to heat flow through the building fabric (walls, windows, roof and floor)
- the rate at which warm inside air is exchanged for cold outside air (providing ventilation)
- the temperature difference between inside and outside.

By cutting down the ability of the fabric to transmit heat (by insulation) and by cutting out unwanted draughts (by draughtproofing), the same temperature difference can be maintained but at a lower rate of heat input. Similarly, if the temperature difference is reduced by setting thermostats lower, that also will reduce the heat input.

heat in   **heat out**

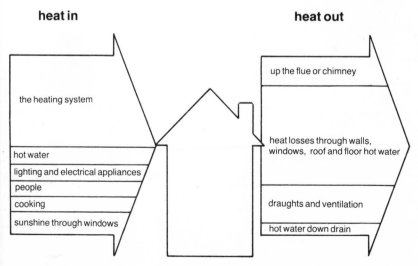

the heating system

hot water

lighting and electrical appliances

people

cooking

sunshine through windows

up the flue or chimney

heat losses through walls, windows, roof and floor hot water

draughts and ventilation

hot water down drain

Insulation

Most older houses, because of their construction, have rather poor thermal insulation. When it is cold outside, the internal surface of walls and windows will also be cold.

With poor levels of insulation not only do you lose more heat:

- cold walls and windows make the room feel colder, even if the air temperature is reasonably warm
- warm room air cools quickly when in contact with cold external surfaces, creating cold downdraughts, chilling the feet and ankles

- the moisture in warm air condenses on cold surfaces, leading to condensation and possibly mould growth.

The effect of adding insulation is to reduce the rate of heat loss through the fabric, with the following benefits:

- warmer interior surfaces
- the warmer surfaces make you *feel* warmer, without turning up the thermostat setting
- you use less fuel to achieve a comfortable temperature
- there is a much lower risk of surface condensation.

Ventilation

A continuous supply of fresh air is essential:

- for breathing
- to remove excessive moisture (see condensation on page 14)
- to supply oxygen for fuel-burning appliances
- to remove smells from cooking and smoking, and to prevent the air becoming stale.

The minimum level of ventilation required for healthy living conditions is the subject of research, but will in any case vary from one household to another. It will depend, for example, on the amount of moisture generated in the home and on the number of smokers.

Evidence suggests that it is sufficient for the air to be changed once every hour (called one air change). In contrast, many older houses have ventilation rates of one and a half air changes an hour. This means that heated air is being unnecessarily replaced by cold outside air. The higher the ventilation rate the more energy is lost in this way.

The ventilation rate varies with the climatic conditions – when it is windy or cold, it increases. The diagram illustrates the large number of leakage paths where air can enter and leave in an uncontrolled way.

Caution

The air supply for fuel-burning appliances *must be maintained* to ensure that complete combustion of the fuel takes place and flue gases are safely drawn up the chimney. So don't block up air bricks or grilles in a room with an open fire or other fuel-burning appliance. (This does not apply to some gas appliances which have a balanced flue, called room sealed appliances – they draw their air directly from outside.)

To seal air paths which cause troublesome draughts and excessive ventilation you should:
- draughtproof windows and doors
- draughtproof suspended timber ground floors and seal the gaps between the skirting and the floor
- draughtproof the trap door into the roof space
- seal gaps and cracks around pipes and cables that pass through the floor, ceiling and external walls
- block up unused fireplaces (but you *must* provide a small air grille to ventilate the chimney, otherwise it could become damp).

Controllable ventilation

The aim of draughtproofing and sealing gaps and cracks is to reduce excessive ventilation. It is essential, however, to provide some controllable ventilation in each room, and in particular, attention should be paid to the ventilation of your kitchen and bathroom. The following measures should be included in your improvement plans where feasible:
- install extract fans to serve your kitchen and bathroom, preferably ones which incorporate a humidistat control. Fans can interfere with the operation of fuel-burning appliances so seek advice from your Gas Board or the Solid Fuel Advisory Service
- provide ventilation in bedroom and living room windows. Ventilators should provide at least 600mm^2 of free area, when fully open, for each 1m^2 of floor area. Ventilation may simply be by means of a top opening light to a window, or a trickle ventilator (see page 84).

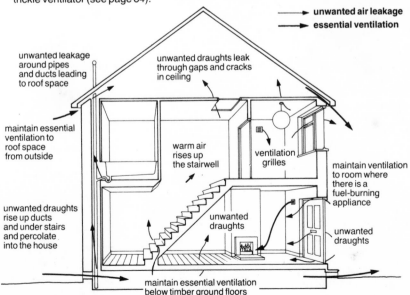

unwanted air leakage

essential ventilation

unwanted leakage around pipes and ducts leading to roof space

unwanted draughts leak through gaps and cracks in ceiling

maintain essential ventilation to roof space from outside

warm air rises up the stairwell

ventilation grilles

maintain ventilation to room where there is a fuel-burning appliance

unwanted draughts rise up ducts and under stairs and percolate into the house

unwanted draughts

unwanted draughts

maintain essential ventilation below timber ground floors

Condensation

Moisture is released into your house in several ways:

- cooking and washing-up
- having a bath
- drying clothes
- from portable paraffin and bottled gas heaters
- breathing.

How condensation occurs

The moisture usually evaporates invisibly into the air. The warmer the air the more moisture it can contain but when warm moist air cools it can no longer hold as much moisture and the excess is deposited on the coldest nearby surface. This explains the condensation on cold window surfaces after a cold night. Cold walls also absorb moisture but this usually evaporates back into the air when temperatures rise again during the day, causing no harm. However, an excessive amount of moisture on cold, poorly insulated surfaces can cause long-term saturation of the plaster. This can result in wallpaper peeling off and mould appearing on walls and ceilings, in cupboards and in severe cases condensation within the building structure.

How to prevent condensation

Condensation can be overcome by a combination of insulation, ventilation, heating and reducing the amount of moisture released into your home.

- Insulation helps the heating to raise the surface temperature inside the rooms and reduces the risk of condensation.
- Ventilation carries away moisture by exchanging warm moist air for drier outside air.
- Heating raises the air temperature, allowing the air to hold more moisture until it can be vented away harmlessly.
- The list in the box suggests some ways in which you can reduce the amount of moisture released inside your home. This should be the first line of attack if your home suffers from condensation
- A vapour barrier prevents moisture entering the building structure (see below).

Ways to reduce the amount of moisture you release in your home:

- keep doors to the kitchen shut when cooking or washing and provide an extract fan over the cooker, or open a window while cooking
- dry clothes outside or, if you have a tumble dryer, vent it to the outside
- when filling a bath, keep the door closed and use an extract fan or, when you have finished, open the window to dispel the moist air and keep the door closed.

What is a vapour barrier?

Where insulation is added internally, a vapour barrier must be placed on the warm side of the insulation to prevent moisture passing through it and condensing on the cooler surfaces behind.
A vapour barrier is a continuous layer of airtight material which prevents water vapour passing through it. The most commonly used material is polythene sheet (125 microns thick – 500 gauge). All joints should be sealed to achieve as complete a vapour barrier as possible. In practice, a perfect seal is not possible because fixings and electrical wiring puncture the barrier. The term *vapour check* is used where a complete seal is not possible.

Special coatings are available for brushing on to form a vapour barrier on plasterboard.

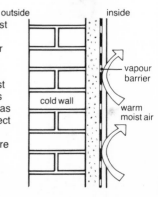

outside — inside
vapour barrier
cold wall
warm moist air

Heating

The design of the heating system should aim to deliver the right amount of heat to the required places as efficiently as possible. It is therefore important to choose a suitable heating system and appropriate controls. *Cutting home energy costs, a step-by-step Monergy guide*, available from the Energy Efficiency Office, should help you to decide which fuel is most economic for your home.

If you are planning to install central heating, here are some suggestions which should help your heating system run at peak efficiency.

● Insulation before sizing boiler and radiators

A well-insulated home needs a smaller heating system and has lower fuel running costs, so before you change your heating system consider the opportunity for installing insulation and draughtproofing measures. Make sure your heating installer takes these plans into account *before* calculating the size of the boilers and radiators.

● Correct sizing of boiler and radiators

Choose a boiler with enough capacity to keep the house warm in cold weather plus some extra capacity to raise the temperature of the house quickly when the system has been off for some time. There is no point in having a large capacity boiler and inadequate radiators. Although radiators should be sized to utilise the full output of the boiler, this will rarely be needed and so there is no need to design extra capacity for the hot water cylinder.

● Position of boiler and hot water cylinder

Aim to position the boiler and hot water cylinder as close to each other as possible, and insulate the connecting pipework. This will reduce unnecessary heat losses, particularly in summer when the boiler is serving only the hot water cylinder. With long uninsulated pipe runs the boiler wastes much of its energy in summer heating up the pipes rather than providing hot water.

● Control of room and hot water temperatures

Good thermostatic controls regulate temperatures and avoid wasteful overheating. Every 1°C rise in the room thermostat setting increases the heating bill by about 6–10 per cent. Programmers and time switches working in conjunction with thermostats and motorised valves make it easier to ensure that the heating is switched on only when needed and that the boiler works at peak efficiency. Topic Sheet 13 describes the range of heating controls available.

Alternative way to heat water

Your central heating system may not be the most economic way to provide hot water during the summer. Your local gas or electricity board will be able to advise on alternatives.

● Partial versus full central heating

In a well-insulated house full central heating may not be necessary. In two-storey houses, the bedrooms benefit from heat rising from the living room to the upper floors, and installing partial central heating may be adequate for you, especially if bedrooms are not used for studying or hobbies. It may be more beneficial to heat only those spaces that it is reasonably necessary to heat. For smaller homes, installing individual heaters will probably work out cheaper, and some heaters are available with a thermostatic control and time clock to ensure good temperature control – see Topic Sheet 13. In single-storey homes where bedrooms are not heated from below, some provision for heating should be provided.

IMPROVEMENT OPPORTUNITY TABLES

The following pages describe the main energy saving opportunities in more detail. The tables compare normal improvement work with more energy efficient alternatives. Opposite the tables are set out any safety aspects and precautions that need to be considered, together with related energy improvements that should be carried out at the same time.

If any of the energy efficient measures interests you, turn to the Topic Sheet(s) listed in the boxes. You can use each Topic Sheet for following how to do the work yourself or for showing a builder or specialist installer how you want the work done.

How to use the tables

In comparing normal and energy efficient improvements, the tables give the typical extra cost of adopting the energy efficient approach, usually in £/m². For example, the typical costs of adding 100mm insulating quilt to a pitched roof of 42m² (if you do the work yourself) are:

£2 × 42m² = £84
(if you employ a builder)
£3.50 × 42m² = £147

The next column in each table gives the likely annual savings in your fuel bill if you adopt the energy efficient improvement. We describe below the assumptions on which these savings are based, and explain how you can make adjustments to take into account your own situation and preferences.

The final two columns indicate how worthwhile the energy efficient improvement is in terms of cost-effectiveness (Good buy) and timing (Good improvement opportunities).

What are the savings based on?

The savings in the tables assume that you have gas central heating and run it during the winter for 9hrs a day on weekdays and 16hrs a day at weekends. They also assume that you heat your living rooms to 21°C (70°F) and the rest of the house to 18°C (64°F). For how to adjust the savings figure to take account of a different thermostat setting, alternative heating patterns and other fuels, see opposite.

What difference would it make if...

...I heated my house for a different number of hours? The following table sets out what effect different central heating patterns will have on the savings.

...I used a different fuel? With a solid fuel room heater, off-peak storage radiators or oil-fired central heating savings may be up to 25 per cent greater than in the improvement opportunities tables.

...I heated my house to a different temperature? Each 1°C (2°F) change in the room thermostat setting will make a difference of between 6 and 10 per cent in your heating costs. The more you use your heating and the warmer you keep your home, the greater will be the impact of a change in the thermostat setting.

Heating on weekdays	Weekends	Change in savings
6hrs/day	6hrs/day	reduced to 45% of savings in table
6hrs/day	9hrs/day	reduced to 55% of savings in table
6hrs/day	16hrs/day	reduced to 65% of savings in table
9hrs/day	9hrs/day	reduced to 90% of savings in table
9hrs/day	16hrs/day	savings as shown in table
16hrs/day	16hrs/day	savings increased by 25%

6 hours a day assumes only evening heating (eg 4pm – 10pm).

9 hours a day assumes only early morning and evening heating (eg 6am – 9am) and 4pm – 10pm)

16 hours a day assumes continuous daytime and evening heating (eg 6am – 10pm)

KEY TO SYMBOLS

■ ■ ■	Excellent short-term investment
■ ■	Good medium-term investment
■	Worth considering if you plan to stay 10 years or more
□	Not cost-effective but improves comfort and may have other advantages, eg low maintenance and may improve the value of the home
★ ★ ★	The opportunity will be missed if you don't act now
★ ★	Excellent opportunity – it will save you money and future disruption if you do the work now
★	Good opportunity (eg while the builder is on site)
☆	Work can be carried out at any time

Note: each area of improvement opportunity is assessed separately — individual measures only compete for points within each table

Type of construction	Measures that comply with 1985 Building Regulations (Part L)	Energy efficient alternative	Typical extra cost /m²	Typical annual saving /m²	Good buy	Good improvement opportunity
Roof	Pitched roof with 100mm mineral wool insulation	Lay 150mm thick loft insulation instead of 100mm	£1.25	8p – 15p	■	★
Walls	Cavity brick wall with part of the cavity filled with insulation	Cavity enlarged to 75mm wide and completely filled with cavity wall insulation. Lightweight block used for inner wall	£1.25	17p – 27p	■	★★★
		Use timber framed inner leaf with 100mm of mineral fibre insulation	60p	17p – 27p	■ ■	★★★
Windows	Single glazed windows, no draughtproofing	Double glazed window with integral draughtproofing, fitted with a trickle ventilator	£55	£3 – £4.60	■	★★★
Floor	Solid concrete floor and screed, finished with vinyl tiles. No insulation	Replace the screed with a laminate of 50mm extruded polystyrene and moisture resistant chipboard finished with floor sealer	£3.75	35p – 70p	■	★★★

Improvement opportunities
NEW EXTENSIONS

New extensions *must* comply with the 1985 Building
Regulations (or the 1983 Building Standards [Scotland]
Regulations) which includes a requirement for a minimum
standard of insulation. However, as the table shows, it is
worthwhile building to a better standard than the Building
Regulations.

Safety and precautions
● If your existing floors are suspended timber and you add
  an extension with a solid floor, you must maintain
  underfloor ventilation to the existing timber floor.

Related energy improvements
● Provide controllable ventilators in all new windows.

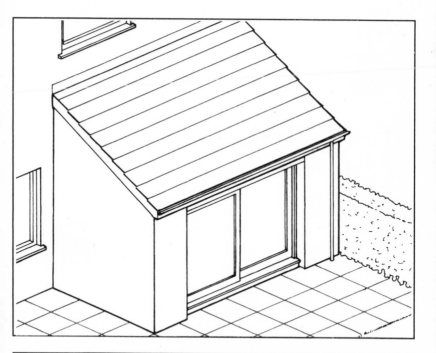

See	Topic Sheet 1	*How to insulate your loft*
	Topic Sheet 4	*Cavity wall insulation*
	Topic Sheet 9	*Double glazing*
	Topic Sheet 12	*Insulating a concrete floor*

Condition	Normal improvement	Energy efficient improvement	Typical cost/m²	Annual saving/ m²	Good buy	Good improvement opportunity
No insulation	None	Add 100mm of loft insulation	DIY £2 builder £4.40	£1 – £1.50	■ ■ ■	☆ ★
		Or add 150mm thick loft insulation (instead of 100mm)	DIY £3.25 builder £6.30	£1.05 – £1.60	■ ■ ■ ■	☆ ★
		Insulate and draughtproof the trap door and into the loft	DIY £6.50 builder £18	£2 – £3	■ ■ ■ ■	☆ ★
25mm of existing insulation	None	Add 100mm of loft insulation on top of the existing insulation	DIY £2 builder £4.40	35p – 52p	■ ■ ■ ■	☆ ★

Improvement opportunities
PITCHED ROOFS

The loft is the easiest and cheapest place in your house to add insulation. If you are applying for an Improvement Grant, your local council will insist that you install 100mm (4in) of loft insulation. If you have no loft insulation or none 30mm thick or more already, you may qualify under the 'Homes Insulation Scheme' for a grant – see page 46 for further details.

Loft insulation is laid between the ceiling joists; 100mm is the minimum thickness you should install. If you use oil or electricity for heating, it will probably be worthwhile putting in at least 150mm.

Safety and precautions

Ventilation
- The effect of adding loft insulation is to reduce winter temperatures of the roof – this increases the risk of condensation in the loft, especially where your roof has been renewed and felt added below the tiles. To combat the risk of condensation you should ensure the roof space is well ventilated at eaves level. Make sure that outside air can ventilate the roof space from the eaves on opposite sides of the roof. Do not tuck insulation into the eaves.

Electrical
- Electrical cables should be kept above the insulation wherever possible. If your house is being rewired, advise the electrician that you are insulating the loft; it may be necessary to de-rate the cables (reduce the amount of current that some of the cables could carry).

- **PVC** insulated cables should not come into contact with expanded polystyrene insulation – otherwise, in the course of time, this will cause embrittlement of the PVC. Keep cables apart and run them through conduit.

Re-roofing
- If you are having your roof re-tiled, make sure your builder uses either traditional sarking felt or a material approved by the British Board of Agrément. Condensation problems have resulted from the use of some polythene-based materials.

Related energy improvements

- If you have a 'room in the roof' you should not only insulate the loft, but also the walls and sloping areas of ceiling – use the 'cold construction' method for flat roofs illustrated on page 49.

- Insulate and draughtproof the trap door into the loft.

- It is essential to insulate all tanks and water pipes in the roof space.

- Gaps and holes in the ceiling are the main ways that moisture from the house enters the loft, and should be sealed, especially over the bathroom.

- Rebalance existing radiators to avoid overheating on the top floor.

See	**Topic Sheet 1**	*How to insulate your loft*
	Topic Sheet 2	*Insulating tanks and pipes*

Condition	Normal improvement	Energy efficient improvement	Typical extra cost/m²		Annual saving /m²	Good buy	Good improvement opportunity
Roof leaks and is in poor condition	Remove existing roof finish and replace with high performance roofing felt and 13mm fibreboard on vapour barrier	As normal approach, but replace fibreboard with a thicker, more effective insulation board eg 50mm polystyrene/13mm fibreboard laminate	*builder*	£4.50	35p–50p	■	★★★
Ceiling needs replacing	Take down existing ceiling and replace with a new plasterboard ceiling; decorate	Push-fit 100mm mineral fibre quilt between the joists and staple a polythene vapour check in place before fixing plasterboard ceiling in normal way	*DIY* *builder*	£3.25 £6.50	65p–£1	■■ ■■	★★★

Improvement opportunities
FLAT ROOFS

Flat roofs are more difficult and expensive to insulate than pitched roofs. The most economic solution depends on whether repair work is needed.

The best place for the insulation is above the roof deck, as this keeps the roof structure warm and greatly lessens the risk of condensation in the roof space. So if your roof covering is in poor condition you should take the opportunity to include a good level of insulation as part of the re-roofing work.

Safety and precautions

- Wherever you place the insulation, you *must* place a vapour barrier or vapour check immediately below it – otherwise moisture will condense on the cold surfaces above the insulation and rot the roof timbers (see Topic Sheet 3 for details).

- If you intend to replace the existing ceiling with a combustible material (eg t&g boarding) then you should use a non-combustible insulation above it, such as mineral (glass or rock) wool quilt. To place expanded polystyrene, for example, above t&g boarding could create a serious fire risk.

- Where insulation is placed directly above a new ceiling, a 50mm (2in) space above the insulation should be cross-ventilated with outside air from openings at the roof perimeter. This ventilation can be difficult to provide.

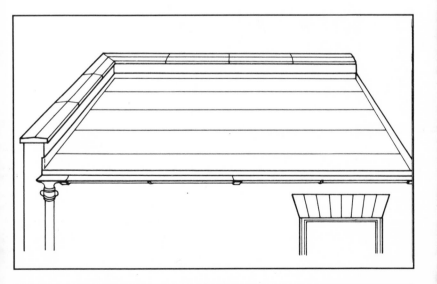

See **Topic Sheet 3** *Insulating a flat roof*

Condition	Normal improvement	Energy efficient improvement	Typical extra cost/m²	Annual saving /m²	Good buy	Good improvement opportunity
Brickwork or render in poor condition; damp due to driving rain	Render the wall and apply a pebbledash finish	Fix an external wall insulation system, including a 25–100mm thermal insulant and render or cladding	*specialist* £20	85p – £1.30	□	★★
Brickwork and plaster sound	Remove old wallpaper, fill cracks and redecorate	Glue 50mm laminate of expanded polystyrene/plasterboard to the existing wall before redecorating	*DIY* £9.50 *builder* £18	90p – £1.35	■ □	★★
Plaster in poor condition	Remove existing plaster, then re-plaster, remove and refix skirting and decorate	Remove existing plaster, batten out the wall, infill with 60mm mineral wool, line with polythene vapour barrier and plasterboard; decorate	*DIY* £8 *builder* £11.50	90p – £1.40	■ ■	★★★
Wall has rising damp	Remove existing plaster and skirting, inject DPC, apply render with waterproof additive and apply skim coat; fix new skirting and decorate	As normal approach, but replace skim coat with 50mm laminate of expanded polystyrene/plasterboard	*builder* £13	90p – £1.35	■	★★

Improvement opportunities
SOLID WALLS

Most houses built before 1930 have solid walls. Solid walls can usually be recognised by the pattern of bricks – there is a regular pattern of full and half length bricks. The wall thickness can be measured at a window opening.

In the 1920s and 1930s many solid walls were rendered, so the pattern of bricks will not be visible, except perhaps below the damp proof course (DPC).

Insulation can either be added to the outside or inside of a solid wall and is usually a job for a builder or specialist contractor. The application of *external* insulation acts like a tea cosy round your house – the insulation keeps the outside walls much warmer and they cool down very slowly after the heating is switched off. Adding insulation to the *inside* of the wall results in the house warming up very quickly when the heating is switched on. With warmer walls your home will feel much more comfortable.

Safety and precautions

- If you insulate walls internally, you must include a vapour barrier on the *warm* side of the insulation (see Topic Sheets 6 and 7).

- If your walls suffer from rising damp, this must be dealt with before adding insulation.

Related energy improvements

- With internal insulation, seal all junctions with floors, ceilings and windows to prevent draughts.

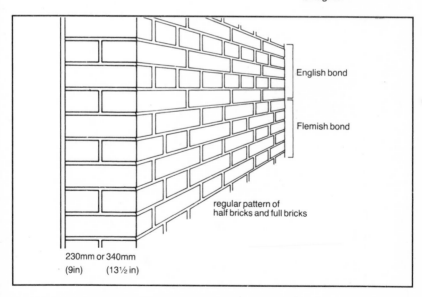

English bond

Flemish bond

regular pattern of half bricks and full bricks

230mm or 340mm
(9in)   (13½ in)

See   **Topic Sheet 5**   *External wall insulation*

Topic Sheet 6   *Internal wall insulation – plasterboard/insulation laminates*

Topic Sheet 7   *Internal wall insulation – timber battens*

Condition	Normal improvement	Energy efficient improvement	Typical extra cost/m²	Annual saving/m²	Good buy	Good improvement opportunity
No damp penetration, brickwork well pointed	None	Cavity insulation by a specialist contractor				
		– UF foam	£4 – £5	60p – £1	■■	☆
		– Polystyrene beads or granules	£5.50 – £7.50	60p – £1	■■	☆
		– Blown mineral (glass or rock) wool	£5.50 – £7.50	60p – £1	■	☆

Safety and precautions

- Despite earlier worries, very few cases of cavity wall insulation have given problems.

- Employ only a specialist installer who uses a material approved by the British Board of Agrément or who is registered by the British Standards Institution. Topic Sheet 4 explains this in more detail.

- Damp penetration is very unlikely if British Standard or British Board of Agrément guidelines on exposure to severe driving rain are followed.

- Although there is only a slight risk of UF foam bringing a very small increase in the level of formaldehyde fumes in the home after the initial short 'curing' stage, this can be enough to produce an allergic reaction in some people. So if anyone in your house reacts badly to everyday chemicals such as cosmetics, use an alternative cavity fill.

- Cavity wall insulation is *not* suitable for timber frame homes.

Improvement opportunities
CAVITY WALLS

Most houses built after 1930 have cavity walls can be recognised by the pattern of bricks – they are nearly all 225mm (9in) long. The wall thickness can be measured at a window opening.

Cavity wall insulation can reduce by two-thirds the amount of heat lost through walls. By keeping the inner wall warmer, it also reduces the risk of condensation. It is cheaper than many other home improvements.

Cavity walls are easier and much cheaper to insulate than solid walls, but you need to call in a specialist firm to carry out the work. The cavity is filled by pumping or blowing insulating material through a series of holes drilled in the brickwork from outside. Several different materials are available and are described in Topic Sheet 4.

Related energy improvements

- Block up any unused air bricks to rooms before the cavity is filled. Do not block up air bricks which ventilate a timber ground floor (see points to consider on page 89).

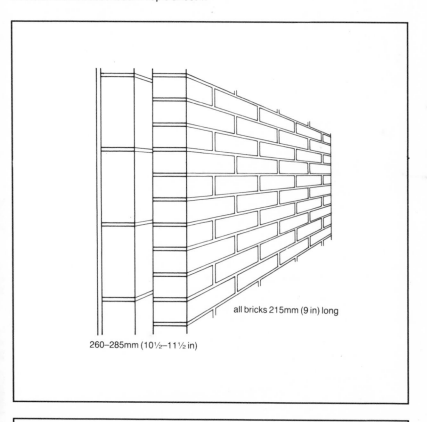

all bricks 215mm (9 in) long

260–285mm (10½–11½ in)

See   **Topic Sheet 4**   *Cavity wall insulation*

27

Condition	Normal improvement	Energy efficient improvement	Typical extra cost per house*	Annual savings per house	Good buy	Good improvement opportunity
Good condition but ill-fitting	Normally just repainted. No energy saving measures except perhaps for cheap DIY draughtproofing	Add good quality draughtproofing	*DIY* £30 *builder* £120	£17 – £26	■ ■	☆ ★
		Or add secondary double glazing (assumes some reduction in draughts)	*DIY* £250 *builder* £1,250	£22 – £25	■ □	☆ ★
Rotten sashes or opening lights, but main frame sound	Replace or repair rotten timber sashes. Overhaul windows and single glaze. Draughtproofing not usually added	Glaze new sashes with sealed double glazing, add draughtproofing and larger balancing weights	*builder* £450	£27 – £41	■	★★
Whole window rotten	Replace windows to match other windows. Single glaze. Draughtproofing not usually added	Double glaze new windows, include draughtproofing and trickle ventilators	*builder* £550	£30 – £46	■	★★★
		Or install uPVC or aluminium replacement glazing, integral draughtproofing and trickle ventilation	*specialist installer* £1,500	£30 – £46	□	★★★

*The table assumes a house with a window area of 10m²

Improvement opportunities
WINDOWS

Draughtproofing and double glazing of windows not only cuts down heat loss, but also make your rooms more comfortable. Cold draughts around the feet and cold 'radiation' from single glazing can make you feel uncomfortable in a room that would otherwise feel warm. Other advantages of double glazing are in cutting down noise and reducing the likelihood of condensation on glazing. It gives some added security against burglars and, in most cases, requires less maintenance. It also adds to the value of your house.

Safety and precautions

Fire

● If you install secondary glazing, make sure you can open or remove it in an emergency – a fire, for example. Remember that plastic glazing cannot be easily broken. If you are replacing your old windows, make sure the new windows have an opening light in each room through which you can climb out in an emergency.

Broken glass

● Ordinary glass is not always suitable where it may get knocked or kicked, particularly by children – for example, in a low picture window. In such a situation plastic glazing or a safety glass should be used – ask your glass merchant for advice.

Ventilation

● A house with too little ventilation is prone to stuffiness and condensation. So if you make a good job of draughtproofing and also seal up other holes and gaps, you should provide controllable trickle ventilation (see Topic Sheet 10). In kitchens and bathrooms, any condensation problems should be overcome by the use of extract fans before double glazing is installed.

● Coal, oil and gas boilers and fires not served by a balanced flue need a supply of fresh air for proper combustion. Make sure that you maintain a fresh air supply in rooms with these appliances.

Related energy improvements

● The use of insulated shutters and heat-reflecting roller blinds at night can also help to reduce heat loss through windows.

● Each room should have a means of providing controllable trickle ventilation (see Topic Sheet 10).

● With double glazing and draughtproofing it is no longer so important to position radiators below windows to counteract cold downdraughts (although the windows will probably still be the coldest surfaces in the room).

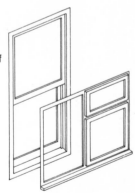

Condition	Normal improvement	Energy efficient improvement	Typical extra cost per door	Annual savings per door	Good buy	Good improvement opportunity
Good condition, but slightly warped	Normally just repainted	Add good quality draughtproofing and a new threshold	DIY £20 builder £35	£3 – £6	■■ ■	☆ ★
		Or form a draught lobby, adding a second door opening across the entrance hall; draughtproof the new door	builder £250	£4 – £7.50	□	★
Door needs replacing	Replace with new timber door. No draughtproofing usually added	Replace with highly insulated door with draughtproofing and new threshold	builder £165	£6 – £10	□	★★

Improvement opportunities
EXTERNAL DOORS

Measurements of air movement have shown that doors are
a major source of draughts, especially where there is no
porch or draught lobby. Making a good job of
draughtproofing should be one of your main priorities and
can improve comfort conditions.

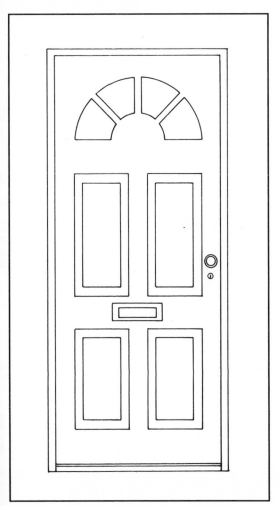

Safety and precautions

- Glass in the lower half of
  doors should be safety
  glass – ask your glass
  merchant for advice.

Related energy improvements

- Don't forget to
  draughtproof the
  letterbox and keyholes.

- Adding a draught lobby
  or enclosed porch not
  only improves your
  home, but also helps to
  reduce draughts.

See **Topic Sheet 8** _Draughtproofing windows and doors_

Condition	Normal improvement	Energy efficient improvement	Typical extra cost		Annual savings	Good buy	Good improvement opportunity
Draughty suspended timber floor	Lay carpet on underlay to cut out draughts	Seal gap between skirting and floorboards with sealant	*DIY*	£12/house	£5 – £8/house	■■	★★
			builder	£55/house		■■	★★
		Or seal gap between skirting and floor boards with timber moulding	*DIY*	£32/house	£5 – £8/house	■■	★★
			builder	£70/house		■	★★
Timber floor in good condition (readily accessible from below)	No work	Insulate from below with 60mm thick mineral fibre quilt supported by netting stapled to the joists	*DIY*	£2.50/m²	50p – 70p/m²	■■	☆
			builder	£6.50/m²		■	★
Timber floor (no access from below), some timber repairs may be necessary	Take up some floorboards to lay services, re-wire etc. May need to take up larger area of floor to replace rotten timber	Take up floorboards push-fit 50mm polystyrene boards between the joists (or place mineral fibre or rolls laid over plastic netting), re-lay floorboards, and seal the skirting with sealant	*builder*	£10.50/m²	60p – 90p/m²	■	★★

Timber floor with extensive rot	Remove all timber and lay new concrete floor, screed and vinyl tiles	builder	£4.25/m²	35p – 70p/m²	■■	★★★
	Replace screed with 50mm polystyrene and moisture resistant chipboard floor finished with floor sealer Or add 50mm thick extruded polystyrene insulation below new concrete floor	builder	£8/m²	35p – 70p/m²	■	★★★

GROUND FLOORS

A warm floor is a major asset, particularly if you walk about in bare feet or have young children.

The opportunities to reduce heat loss through floors depend on whether the floor is suspended timber or solid concrete. With an old timber floor, reducing the draughts should be the first priority. Adding insulation below the floorboards will be worthwhile provided it can be carried out easily.

There are very few opportunities to add insulation to a solid floor but Topic Sheet 12 will give you some ideas.

Related energy improvements

- Laying underlay below a carpet helps to cut out draughts and makes the floor feel warmer.

- Hardboard fixed to floorboards eliminates draughts and is in any case usually necessary before laying vinyl tiles or sheet.

- You should insulate all water pipes (including central heating pipes) running below the floor, or reroute them above floor level.

Essential precautions
- Maintain ventilation below suspended timber floors. Don't block air bricks to timber ground floors.

- Don't pile soil or lay new paths above the damp proof course level. The DPC should be at least 150mm (6 in) above the outside ground level.

- Make sure you maintain easy access to essential services located under the floor. This may mean forming panels above stopcocks etc. Even better, relocate such control valves above the floor.

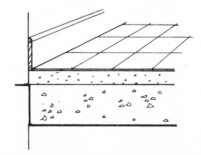

See	**Topic Sheet 11**	*Timber floors*
	Topic Sheet 12	*Insulating a concrete floor*

Heating or hot water system	Energy efficient design	Typical extra cost	Typical annual saving	Good buy	Good improvement opportunity
Hot water cylinder	Add an 80mm thick jacket to an uninsulated hot water cylinder, or buy a cylinder with factory applied foam insulation	*DIY* £6.50 *builder* £16	£12 – £18	■■ ■■	☆ ★
	Add an 80mm thick jacket on top of a cylinder with factory applied foam insulation	*DIY* £6.50 *builder* £16	£2 – £4	■■ ■■	☆ ★
Central heating system with radiators	Add reflective foil behind radiators (for five radiators)	*DIY* £10 *builder* £25	£4 – £12	■■ ■■	☆ ★
	Add thermostats and motorised valve to provide separate control of water and room temperatures	*heating installer* £175	£25 – £35		★★★
	Replace an old (10 years) boiler, when it next goes wrong, with an efficient new one	*heating installer* £550 – £700	£80 – £150	■	★★★
	Instead of a conventional gas boiler, install a condensing boiler	*heating installer* £200 – £250	£30 – £60	■	★★★
	Add thermostatic radiator valves to radiators	*heating installer* £100	£6 – £12	■	★★
Off-peak electric storage radiators	Add an outside temperature sensor to control overnight charge to radiators	*heating installer* £100	£30 – £45	■	★★

Improvement opportunities

HEATING AND
HOT WATER CONTROLS

To make efficient use of your heating and keep your house comfortable, a good standard of insulation is only half the answer. You also need to be able to control your heating effectively so that you get heat when and where you want it and avoid rooms overheating, which is very expensive.

Most central heating boilers have their own internal thermostats. In addition, you should have at least a room thermostat to control room temperatures and a time switch or programmer to turn the heating on and off at the times you select. A cylinder thermostat on your hot water cylinder will control the hot water temperature but may be expensive to install and therefore not cost-effective.

ENERGY RELATED IMPROVEMENTS

● Insulate your hot water cylinder and hot pipes leading from it to taps. This is the most cost-effective insulation measure of all.

● Insulate central heating pipes leading through unheated spaces unless you prefer the pipes to give background heating.

● Add reflective foil behind radiators on external walls – this is a cheap but very effective measure, particularly where the wall has not been insulated. A shelf over the radiator also helps by preventing warmed air rising straight up to the ceiling. Do not cover radiators with curtains.

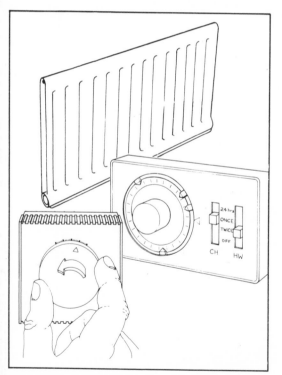

| See | **Topic Sheet 2** | *Insulating cisterns and pipes* |
| | **Topic Sheet 13** | *Selecting heating appliances and controls* |

TOPIC SHEETS

TOPIC SHEETS

The thirteen Topic Sheets describe in greater detail the energy efficient construction methods listed in the Improvement Opportunity tables.

The Topic Sheets are designed to be useful to both the DIY home improver and those employing a builder to do the work for them. As a quick reference, each job is coded to show how easy it is to do yourself, or to indicate if a specialist must be called in.

An easy job requiring few tools – within the scope of most householders

Not too difficult, but requires some DIY experience

Should be tackled only by the dedicated DIY enthusiast. Most people will call in a builder

Should be tackled only by the dedicated DIY enthusiast. Most people will call in a specialist

A job for a specialist installer only.

Employing a builder

Many of the Topic Sheets illustrate work which may look new and unfamiliar not only to you, but also to your builder. Some builders who carry out home improvement work may not be aware of the newer energy saving improvements shown in the Topic Sheets.

Don't be put off if the work looks complicated. Show the Topic Sheet to your builder to indicate what work you want done *and* use it yourself to check that the builder does the job properly and takes account of any safety or precautionary notes. Make sure that the builder gives you an estimate of cost before beginning any work.

Calling in a specialist

Some energy saving improvements require specialist equipment or skill and are beyond the scope of both the small builder and the DIY enthusiast.
Where you need to call in a specialist the Topic Sheet lists the points you should consider and discuss with your architect, surveyor or specialist installer. Some Topic Sheets also list the energy saving features you should ask about or offer advice on what features are likely to be worth including in your improvement plans.

HOW TO INSULATE YOUR LOFT

In most cases, using the right materials, the work is within the capability of the 'do-it-yourself' householder. Any manufacturer's instructions provided with the materials should be studied carefully and carried out. Alternatively, you can employ a specialist contractor to supply the material and do the job for you. Some materials need to be blown into place by a machine, work for a specialist contractor only.

Insulating materials

Mineral wool mats and DIY loose-fills can be bought from builders' and plumbers' merchants and DIY stockists. Mineral fibre is usually sold in rolls 400mm (16in) wide. The most common thickness is 100mm (4in) but greater thicknesses are becoming more widely available. The insulation should be at least 100mm (4in) thick, even if you already have a 25mm (1in) layer.

Loose-fill materials blown into the loft are usually mineral wool or cellulose fibres. They have the same insulation value as rolls of loft insulation and should have a minimum finished thickness of 100mm (4in).

DIY loose-fill materials, usually vermiculite, are sold in bags and should be poured between the joists to the depths recommended. They are useful if your loft has awkward corners or obstructions or if the joist spacing is irregular, but are much more expensive than rolls of insulation, and need to be about 60 per cent deeper to provide the same level of insulation.

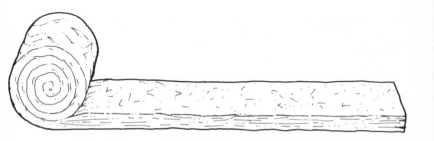

Before you start work in the loft

1. If your loft has a trap door and you are using a step-ladder, remember to tie the ladder firmly in place or get someone to hold it while you are using it. If there is no way into the loft, get a builder to make you a permanent hatch.

2. Get a torch or a proper inspection lamp in a wire cage and a piece of board that will reach across at least three joists. The ceiling between the joists is very weak and will not carry your weight – so stand on the board or timber joists, *never* on the ceiling.

3. Measure the distance between the ceiling joists; and their length; count the number of joist spaces to work out how much insulation roll you will need.

4. Locate the pipes and water tanks and measure the tank. When adding loft insulation it is essential to insulate the cistern and pipework (see Topic Sheet 2).

5. Check the sizes and lengths of water pipe which will remain above your loft insulation including the overflows and expansion pipes.

6. If you intend to use a loose-fill material, to insulate to a depth of 150mm (6in) you would need 150 litres per square metre. Make sure that the depth of the ceiling joists is adequate so that freedom of movement, for example access to tanks, can be maintained. You could increase the height of the

joists by nailing strips of wood to the top of the joists before fixing boarding, but it might be simpler to use an alternative insulating material which would not need to be as thick to achieve the recommended level of insulation.

7. Condensation occurring in lofts can cause damage to timber, so make sure there is always plenty of ventilation. If there are chinks of daylight at the eaves or if you can see the tiles and slates in the roof space, and the loft isn't musty, you will probably not need to do anything more to the roof. But if the roof is boarded or felted under the tiles so that you can't see them, you must ensure that eaves ventilation is provided (see opposite).

Laying mineral fibre roll

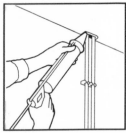

The surface should be clean before you begin to unroll the insulation, so get rid of layers of dust and any shavings left by builders. You should also seal any cracks and gaps around pipes and cables where they go through the ceiling.

Put a piece of board reaching across three joists and stand or kneel safely on it. Starting at the eaves, unroll the insulating material between the joists, moving towards the centre of the left. Make sure you have a gap at the eaves for ventilation.

Cut the roll at the centre of the loft and push lightly down between the joists. Start again from the opposite side of loft. Cut and butt the ends closely together where the lengths meet in the middle. Continue until the whole area is covered. Do not insulate under the cold water cistern.

8. Cracks and holes in the ceiling should always be stopped up before laying the insulation. They cause heat loss by allowing warm moist air to reach the loft, which can lead to condensation problems.

9. While you are in the loft, it is sensible to look out for other problems which might require attention – particularly your electric wiring, which should be kept clear of loft insulation. If you place insulation over or next to wiring – even new wiring – the cables can then carry less current before becoming hot and possibly catching fire. It would therefore be wise to get a competent person (such as someone from your local Electricity Board) to check the wiring before you

insulate. It would also be a good idea to have loft plumbing checked. A building surveyor or architect will be able to offer this advice but may charge a fee.

10. If you are using an insulation roll, cut the ends at the eaves to make sure of unobstructed ventilation. If you are laying loose-fill, pour the contents of the bag between the joists and, provided that the required depth of fill does not exceed the depth of the joists, you will be able to level it with a piece of board. As with all kinds of insulation, make sure it doesn't block the ventilation at the eaves or run down into cavities or holes. This may mean fitting boards to retain the

fill. Proprietary products which retain the insulation at the eaves are available from some building merchants.

11. Loft insulation is made of fibres and can irritate some people's skin so should be installed with care. Don't open the package until you are in the loft, and unroll or pour out the material gently so that loose fibres are not blown about. Wear a simple dust mask and rubber gloves. Once the job is completed, any skin irritation can be lessened by rinsing hands under running water before washing.

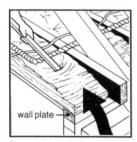

If possible, cut the insulation to pass under wires, being careful not to stretch or damage them. Push the insulation along the ceiling until it covers the top of the wall plate, but remember not to seal the eaves completely.

wall plate

Don't forget to fix a piece of insulating material on to the top of your loft trap door. If you are using mineral fibre, wrap it in polythene to make it easier to handle. Make sure that the trap door fits properly, and draughtproof it with a good quality draughtstrip. It may then need a catch or bolt to keep it tightly shut.

If the roof is boarded or felted under the tiles, so that you cannot see them, it is essential to make a gap or holes at the eaves to allow ventilation to your roof space. The gaps should have at least the same area as a continuous 10mm (3/8in) slot at eaves level – this is the standard of ventilation required by the Building Regulations 1985 for new roofs.

Laying loose fill

Loose-fill insulation is simply poured from the bag between the joists, and smoothed over with a board which is cut to give the right depth when resting on the joists. To reach into corners, nail a board to a broomstick.

Most ceiling joists are 100mm (4in) deep, so filling level with the top gives only about 60 per cent the insulation value of 100mm thick mineral fibre. To comply with the Homes Insulation Scheme you will probably have to cover the joists with insulation – this is not a good idea. Loose-fill may tend to be blown about, and is awkward to finish at the eaves whilst still providing ventilation.

It is worth examining the loft sometime after adding insulation to check that ventilation is adequate, and that there are no signs of condensation. This is best done after a spell of cold weather when the risk of condensation is greatest.

Note: The Homes Insulation Scheme covers the insulation work described in this Topic Sheet – see page 46 for details.

TOPIC 2 INSULATING TANKS AND PIPES

One result of laying insulation in the loft is that the loft itself will get colder. Tanks and pipes within the loft will be liable to freeze up in cold weather, and for this reason they must be insulated.

All cold storage tanks in the loft, including central heating expansion tanks, and all water pipes, including overflows, must be insulated. Do not insulate under the tanks *unless* they are situated well above the ceiling joists, since warmth from below should help prevent the tanks freezing. The recommended thicknesses

of at least 25mm (1 in) for water tank and pipe insulation should greatly reduce the risk of freezing in normal circumstances. In exposed houses in northern areas, 50mm thickness of insulation is advisable.

Where tanks are raised up in the loft, and do not benefit from heat rising from the house, it may be worthwhile fitting electric trace tape connected to a frost-protection thermostat. The thermostat is set to a few degrees above freezing and switches on a low level heating element in the tape when the

temperature drops below freezing.

Systems can be designed to work with a low head of water: for example, many flats have central heating expansion and cold water tanks in the kitchen cupboard area. It is worth considering whether all the pipework could be removed from the roof space when installing a new system.

Roof insulation is another alternative – more expensive than loft insulation but simpler than moving all the pipework out of the loft.

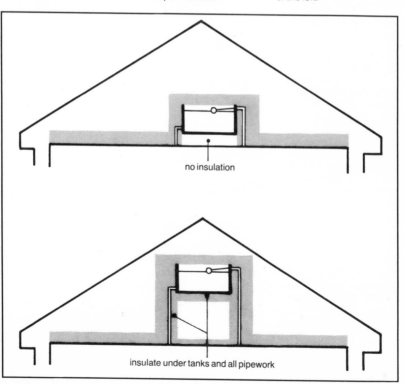

no insulation

insulate under tanks and all pipework

Insulating your cold water tank

Using insulation boards

You can buy pre-cut packs of sheet insulation material to fit the more common sizes of water tank, or you can cut your own casing out of standard sized sheets. The recommended thickness is 25mm (1in). Secure the panels with wire, string or tape.

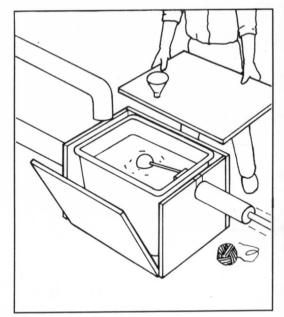

Using mineral (glass or rock) wool mat

It is also possible to use mineral (glass or rock) wool mat quilting secured with wire, tape or string. Take care that fibres do not get into the tank.

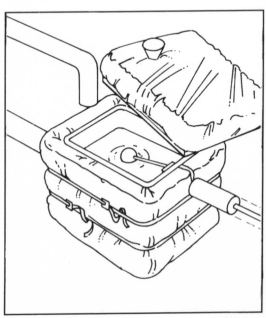

Insulating water pipes in the loft

All water pipes in the loft (including overflows) should be insulated. The only exceptions are those pipes that are within or under the loft insulation or within the tank casing. If you are using rolls of mineral (glass or rock) wool mat, wrap it 'bandage fashion', securing it with wire, tape or string. Don't leave any gaps, and wrap up the bodies of taps and joints as well. You can also use pre-formed moulded insulation which is easier to fit on straight pipe runs, but more difficult around fittings and bends, where it should be taped up.

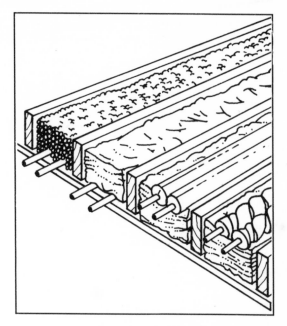

HOT WATER FEED

Insulating your hot water cylinder

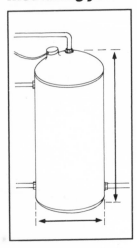

Cylinder jackets are made in a range of standard sizes. You should measure the vertical height of the tank to the top of the dome, as well as the diameter, so that you buy the correct size jacket. Typical standard sizes are 900mm x 450mm and 1050mm x 450mm. Before you buy a cylinder jacket look for a statement that it conforms to British Standards BS 5615:1978. One way of guaranteeing this is to look out for the Kitemark.

Most cylinder jackets are made up of a number of segments held together by a cord tied around the top of the cylinder. Follow the manufacturer's instructions for fixing the jacket. Smooth the jacket down over the cylinder but do not press on it. Wrap one of the belts around the jacket,

close to the top, and fasten it loosely. Fasten the second belt lightly near the bottom of the tank. If there is a third belt fasten it round the middle. Make sure there are no gaps between the jacket sections, which could let heat escape.

If you have an electric immersion heater, ensure that you do not cover the cap or the electric cables. (Electric immersion heaters should always have a wired-in connection rather than a plug and socket.) New cylinders are available with factory applied foam. These are less bulky than a cylinder with an insulated jacket and may be easier to accommodate in a small airing cupboard. Remember that hot water pipes also lose heat, so insulate these as well.

Insulated pipes and a double jacket on the cylinder will allow just enough heat to keep the cupboard warm.

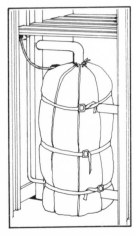

Homes Insulation Scheme

The Scheme provides for a grant towards the cost of installing insulation in lofts where there is none 30mm thick or more already. It also covers the insulation of water tanks and pipes in lofts, and of uninsulated hot water pipes in lofts, and of uninsulated hot water cylinders wherever they are located.

Where there is no access to the loft, the cost of cutting a temporary one will also be eligible for a grant. You can get 66 per cent of the cost of all the material and work, or £69, whichever is the smaller. Elderly or severely disabled applicants on low incomes can get a 90 per cent grant rate with a £95 maximum.

Contact your local council offices for an application form but do not start work before the local authority notifies you that you may do so.

To be eligible for a grant, you must use only the loft insulation materials on the list your local council will give you. You must install at least the thickness specified on the list. You may install greater thicknesses but you will not be paid a grant for the extra amount.

The Scheme is generally not applicable to flat roofs or to other areas of roof where to add insulation would result in insufficient ventilation above the insulation.

There are two alternative positions for adding insulation to a flat roof: above the roof deck, called a *warm* roof deck; and between the joists, called a *cold* roof deck.

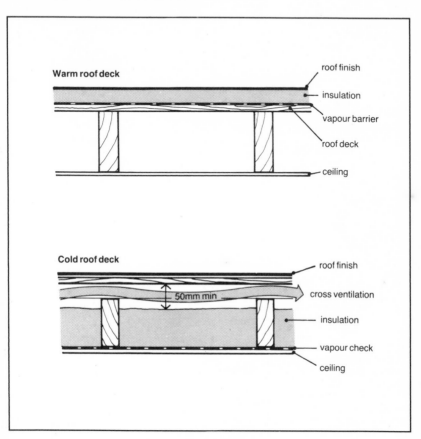

Warm roof deck
- roof finish
- insulation
- vapour barrier
- roof deck
- ceiling

Cold roof deck
- roof finish
- 50mm min
- cross ventilation
- insulation
- vapour check
- ceiling

The method you choose will depend on what repairs are necessary. If the existing roof leaks and is in poor condition, the best option is to go for the 'warm' roof and include insulation as part of the re-roofing work.

If the roof looks to be in good condition or has recently had a new finish applied, it will be more economic to go for the 'cold' roof construction, especially where the ceiling needs to be taken down as part of the improvement work. But you *must* take precautions to prevent condensation – see under Cold roof construction. If it is impossible to provide the recommended ventilation, the best method is to add insulation on top of the existing roof finish – see over.

Warm roof deck construction

This is the best method of insulating a flat roof, and is a job for a specialist roofing contractor. Even where you are employing a builder to carry out major improvement work, he will almost certainly call in a specialist roofing contractor for re-roofing work.

Where the existing roof finish has extensive blisters or leaks badly it will probably be necessary to remove the existing roof finish and lay a completely new finish, starting with a new vapour barrier. But where the existing roof covering is in reasonable condition, it can be retained to act as the vapour barrier itself. Insulation is then bonded to the existing roof, and finished with roofing felt in the usual way. Make sure that the perimeter upstands are high enough to accommodate the extra thickness of the insulation.

There have been several developments in roofing materials in the past few years, such as new high performance felts, which although more expensive, are claimed to be more durable and trouble-free than the traditional three layers of felt. They are designed to accommodate the movement stresses set up by the insulation layer and are recommended for use in warm roof construction. Discuss the choice of roof finishes and insulation with several roofing contractors. Get their views and ask for alternative prices.

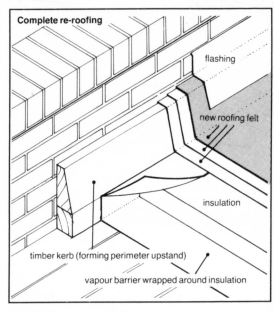

Complete re-roofing

flashing

new roofing felt

insulation

timber kerb (forming perimeter upstand)

vapour barrier wrapped around insulation

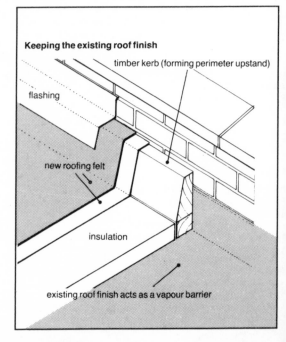

Keeping the existing roof finish

timber kerb (forming perimeter upstand)

flashing

new roofing felt

insulation

existing roof finish acts as a vapour barrier

Cold roof deck construction

This job should be within the scope of the DIY enthusiast, but it involves taking down and replacing the existing ceiling. For this reason you may prefer to leave the job to a builder, but satisfy yourself that he knows how to avoid introducing condensation in the roof space.

Two essential precautions should be taken to minimise the condensation risk:

● add a vapour check (see page 14) to the warm side of the insulation

● ensure that there is adequate ventilation on the cold side of the insulation

The vapour check is usually a polythene sheet (125 microns thick) which is available up to 4m wide so that in most rooms it is possible to fix it in one piece, avoiding any joints. Holes and joints are weak points in the vapour check and should be avoided where possible – for example, consider installing wall lights instead of a ceiling light. Where holes for pipes or wires are unavoidable, cut the hole as small as possible and tape with polythene tape. This will minimise the amount of water vapour that escapes into the roof space.

After adding insulation, the winter temperature of the roof structure above the insulation will be lower, and this increases the risk of condensation. Providing good cross-ventilation will

help to prevent a build-up of moisture. It is recommended that the minimum size of the ventilation holes on opposite sides of the roof are 1/250 the area of the

roof. On a roof spanning 3m (10ft) this would be the equivalent of a 12mm (1/2in) continuous gap along opposite sides of the roof.

Adding insulation under the ceiling

An alternative form of cold construction is to add insulation and a new ceiling below the existing ceiling. The advantage is that you don't have to take down the existing ceiling, but the thickness of insulation is limited by the depth of the new timber battens. In addition, you should consider whether the existing roof can carry the extra weight – if the ceiling is already sagging, adding extra weight is not a good idea. Also check on the ceiling height – in living rooms and bedrooms it should be at least 2.3m to comply with the Building Regulations. Unless taking down the existing ceiling will cause unacceptable disruption, it is probably better to insulate between the joists, especially as it is possible at the same time to check on the condition of the timbers and ensure that it is possible to provide adequate cross-ventilation.

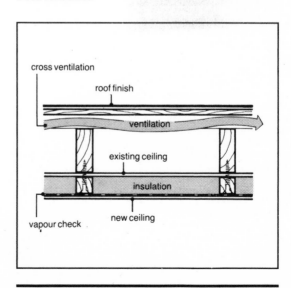

Insulating a flat roof from below

Take down the existing ceiling. Inspect the timbers for rot, especially where they are built into the wall. Add air bricks to provide sufficient ventilation. Drill holes in the joists where there is no other means of ventilation between the joists. To avoid weakening the joists, the holes should be drilled at the mid height. With shallow joists this will limit the thickness of insulation.

Where the roof has a fascia board, instead of adding air bricks, drill holes in the fascia or soffit board, and cover the holes with insect mesh to prevent wasps and bees getting in.

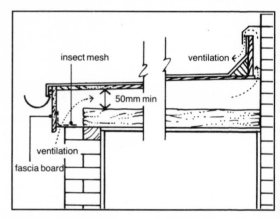

insect mesh

ventilation ←

50mm min

ventilation

fascia board

Push-fit the mineral wool mat or polystyrene boards between the joists. Select a thickness that will leave an air space of 50mm (2in) above the insulation for ventilation. Make sure that there is a clear ventilation route above the insulation and that air bricks are not covered with insulation. Take care not to block the air bricks with the insulation.

Staple the polythene vapour barrier in place, starting from one side of the room. Unroll the polythene sheet on the floor, cutting it square and to size before lifting it up to the ceiling in one piece.

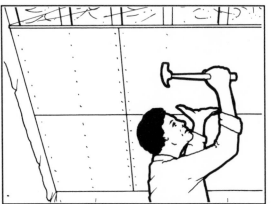

Buy small sheets of plasterboard (about 1.35m long x 0.9m wide) as they are easier to handle and hold in place while you hammer in the galvanised plasterboard nails. Where boards meet they should be sealed with joint filler and taped over. It is easier to get a level finish at the joints if you use 'tapered edge' boards. Getting a good finish is a skilled job and you may wish to get a professional plasterer to apply the finishing touches.

Alternatively, finish the ceiling with t&g boarding, but note that you must use a non-combustible insulation (such as mineral fibre) – otherwise you will increase the fire hazard.

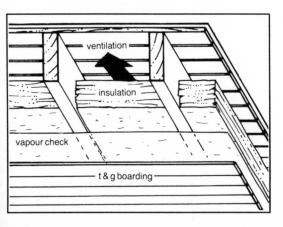

ventilation

insulation

vapour check

t & g boarding

If your house has cavity walls, insulating the cavity is one of the best ways of cutting your heating bills.

Existing cavity walls are insulated by drilling a series of holes in the brickwork and either pumping or blowing insulation through them into the cavity. The job usually only takes from a half to two days and must be carried out by a specialist firm.

The three types of material used for cavity wall insulation are described below.

Polystyrene beads and granules

Two main methods are used. One uses beads which are coated with an adhesive as they are blown into the cavity. This sticks the beads together, and prevents loose beads pouring out if the wall is opened in the future. The second method uses irregular shaped granules of polystyrene or polyurethene.

The size and spacing of the holes depends on the installer. Generally, methods involve drilling either a large number of small holes (25mm diameter) spaced at about one metre intervals, or fewer but larger holes (65mm diameter, or removal of whole bricks) up to 8m apart.

Blown mineral fibre

These may be either glass wool or rock wool, both of which are water repellent and are injected directly into the cavity. The variation in size and spacing of holes is similar to polystyrene beads and granules.

Urea formaldehyde foam

This is mixed together on site from UF resin, hardener and water. The hardener incorporates a foaming agent and just before injection into the cavity the resin and hardener are mixed. The foam sets in the cavity then slowly dries by evaporation through the wall over a number of weeks. As the

foam dries formaldehyde gas is given off. With normal cavity walls which are plastered on the inside, the risk of formaldehyde entering the occupied spaces is low provided that the walls are of sound construction.
If you use an approved installer who follows the recommendations of British Standards 5617 and 5618 you should have no worry about the safety of UF foam cavity insulation. Many homes with new furniture register higher levels of formaldehyde than homes with UF foam cavity insulation. This is because formaldehyde resin is also used as a glue in making chipboard.
UF foam is not suitable for houses in areas of the country which are subject to heavy driving rain. The contractor will be able to advise you on this.

Choosing a contractor

Make sure that the firm you go to for your cavity insulation is an approved contractor.

– If you decide on UF foam, the installer should be registered by the British Standards Institution as an approved firm, and be prepared to guarantee that the work complies with the stringent requirements of British Standard 5618, as updated. The names of approved firms can be obtained from the British Standards Institution.

– For other materials, the work should be carried out to comply with a current Agrément Certificate, or be licensed by a manufacturer who has an Agrément Certificate for his insulation material. In either case, check that they can provide you with a copy of the certificate.

The cavity insulation business is very competitive with dozens of registered installers, so get several estimates. You can get a list of installers from the Trade Associations on page 111. When the surveyor calls round get him to check the condition of the walls and ask for a written statement that they are suitable for the proposed type of cavity wall insulation.

Check that the firm will give you a long-term guarantee, and that it can be transferred to future owners.

To comply with the Building Regulations, your local authority must be told that you plan to install cavity insulation. Reputable firms should notify the local authority automatically. Check that they do so and ask for a copy of the notification.

Note: If your cavity walls show signs of dampness on the inside, you *must* investigate and cure the problem before installing cavity wall insulation.

Building a new cavity wall

If you are extending your home, you will almost certainly use cavity construction for the new walls, which must include a reasonable level of insulation in order to comply with the Building Regulations (1985). Even so, because it is relatively cheap and easy to insulate a cavity wall while it is being built, it will probably be worthwhile building in more insulation than the minimum required.

The two wall constructions illustrated overleaf have twice the insulation value required by the Building Regulations, and yet they cost only a fraction more to build.

Increasing the traditional cavity from 50mm to 75mm and filling it with insulation will greatly reduce the heat loss through the wall. Purpose-made slabs of mineral wool insulation are placed in the cavity as the wall is built. Care is needed to avoid mortar droppings collecting on the insulation as they can provide a path for dampness. Alternatively, mineral wool fibre, polystyrene beads or UF foam can be injected at a later stage. A lightweight block should be used for the inner skin – the lighter the block, the better the insulation value.

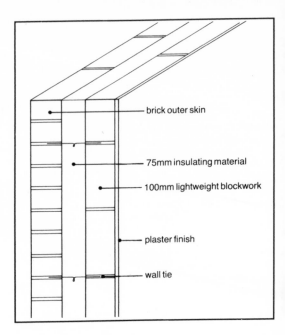

- brick outer skin
- 75mm insulating material
- 100mm lightweight blockwork
- plaster finish
- wall tie

Timber framed construction is still relatively new to most small builders, who are unfamiliar with the details that ensure that timber members stay dry and structurally stable.

However, timber framed construction is quick to erect and can readily incorporate 100mm of insulation *and* maintain a cavity against driving rain. It is essential to include a vapour check as shown. If you know a builder who is familiar with timber frame it might be worth considering.

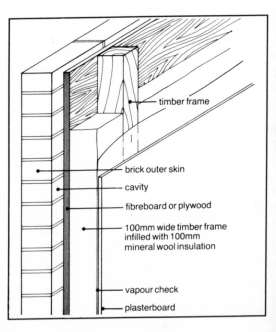

- timber frame
- brick outer skin
- cavity
- fibreboard or plywood
- 100mm wide timber frame infilled with 100mm mineral wool insulation
- vapour check
- plasterboard

EXTERNAL WALL INSULATION

External wall insulation is one of the most expensive types of wall insulation and a job for a specialist contractor only. Because of the high cost, this type of insulation is usually contemplated only where the existing wall is in poor condition and needs extensive repair work (such as rendering to overcome rain penetration). The External Wall Insulation Association will send you a list of their members and descriptions of the systems they offer (see page 111).

Most systems consist of a thermal insulant covered by a reinforcing mesh to provide a key for a protective coat of render or cladding. The surface finishes available range from pebbledash to painted, textured finishes.

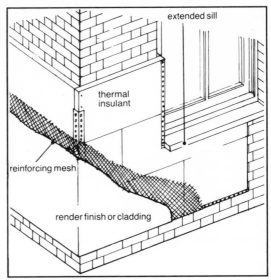

The insulation is usually 25mm to 50mm thick. Increasing the thickness to 100mm costs relatively little but can present problems around windows, rainwater pipes and at roof level.

Points to consider

● **Appearance**
Unless your house is already rendered, its appearance will alter considerably and you may need to get planning permission. If the brickwork or render on your house has deteriorated or is badly weathered, adding external insulation should improve its appearance dramatically.

● **Ornamental detail**
External insulation is not suitable where there is a lot of fine architectural detailing and moulding.

● **Weather protection**
If your walls are in poor condition and there is evidence of dampness from driving rain, external insulation will keep them warmer and drier, but the walls could take 12 months or more to dry out completely. A good overhang at roof level will help to protect the new wall finish. It you are re-roofing consider extending the roof overhang, especially at gable walls.

● **Windows**
Unless windows are being replaced, window sills will need to be extended to shed water clear of the new wall finish. Cutting the insulation around balanced flues, and removing and refixing rainwater pipes, drainage pipes, and telephone cables etc, will increase costs. Insulation should be taken into window reveals – otherwise an existing cold bridge will be made worse and may cause condensation on window reveals.

- **Shrubs and climbers** These will almost certainly need to be cut back in order to apply the external insulation.

- **Future maintenance** A painted decorative finish to the render will need repainting every few years if it is not to deteriorate as a result of the weather. A textured surface is much better at hiding irregularities and tends to weather better than a smooth even render.

- **Structure** Check that the structure is sound before applying external insulation. This is particularly important for houses built with an industrialised system.

Discuss these points with your architect or surveyor and the insulation contractor before coming to a final decision.

Weatherboarding and tile hanging

As an alternative to render weatherboarding or tile hanging can be fixed on battens infilled with insulation, but this is more expensive than render, and needs greater care at windows and corners to keep out the rain. Tile hanging is best confined to upper storeys as it is vulnerable to damage at ground floor level. Where your house already has weatherboarding or tile hanging that needs replacing, consider adding insulation behind the new cladding.

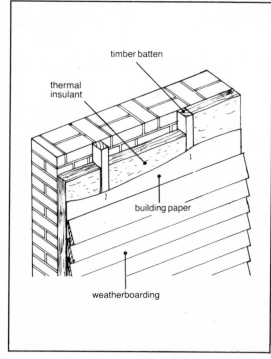

timber batten

thermal insulant

building paper

weatherboarding

PLASTERBOARD/INSULATION LAMINATES

This is the first way of insulating the inside of walls. The second method, using timber battens, is described in Topic Sheet 7.

Plasterboard/insulation laminates consist of boards of plasterboard with a backing of insulation and a built-in vapour check. They are commonly called thermal boards and are not normally stocked by builder's merchants, so you will probably have to order them specially.

If you decide on this form of insulation and your builder has not used it before, suggest to him that he call in a firm of plasterers who have experience of fixing thermal boards – you will probably end up with a neater job. For the DIY enthusiast, the main drawback is in making an acceptable job of joining the boards.

The most commonly available thermal boards have a backing of expanded polystyrene insulation, but other materials such as urethane foam are also available. These other insulation materials tend to be more expensive than polystyrene, but do have some advantages. For example, the better insulating qualities of urethane foam mean that thinner boards can be used to achieve the same level of insulation – this may be important where space is tight, in a small bedroom, for example.

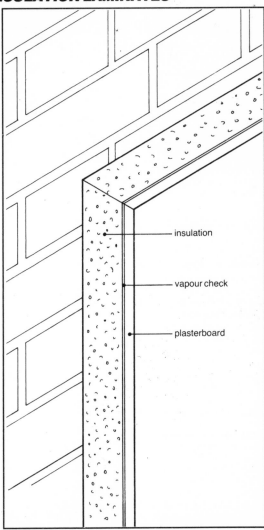

- insulation
- vapour check
- plasterboard

Boards are usually 2.4m long and 1.2m wide. The insulation is available in a range of thicknesses from 12mm up to about 50mm. To obtain the maximum benefit, buy the greatest thickness you can readily accommodate but consider how to finish off the lining at windows and door openings and at decorative mouldings.

Fixing methods

The most appropriate method of fixing the board will depend on the condition of the existing plaster or brickwork.

This method is suitable only where the existing plaster is even and in good condition. Each board is fixed directly to the plaster with adhesive, with nine plugged and screwed fixings to secure the board in case of fire. Laminated boards often tend to bow and need a strong mid-height fixing.

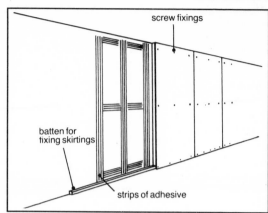

screw fixings

batten for fixing skirtings

strips of adhesive

This is the method to use where the existing wall has been stripped of plaster. The board is bonded to the wall by plaster dabs; nine plugged and screwed fixings secure the board in case of fire. A job for a professional plasterer only.

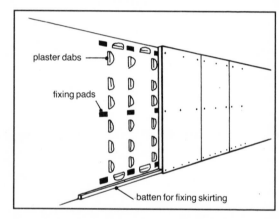

plaster dabs

fixing pads

batten for fixing skirting

For uneven brickwork or walls with a damp proof coating. The board is screwed to metal firrings bonded to the wall. This is more expensive than using plaster dabs, but the damp proofing treatment does not get penetrated by any fixings.

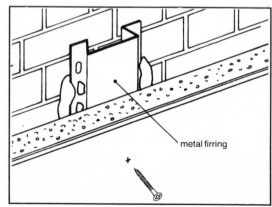

metal firring

Preparing to fix with adhesive

1. Prepare the wall by removing old wallpaper and any flaking paint etc. Remove the skirting board carefully so that it can be refixed to the new wall lining and match up with the skirtings in rest of the room.

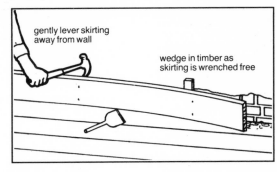

gently lever skirting away from wall

wedge in timber as skirting is wrenched free

2. To provide a fixing for the skirting, a continuous batten, the same thickness as the insulation backing, should be plugged and screwed to the wall at floor level. If the skirting is more than about 150mm high, it is better to fix short vertical battens to the wall and mark their positions on the floor so you know where they are when the thermal board is in place.
Plan where radiators and other heavy fixtures such as shelves are going so that you can make use of the same battens. Ideally, all timber covered by the thermal board should be treated with preservative.

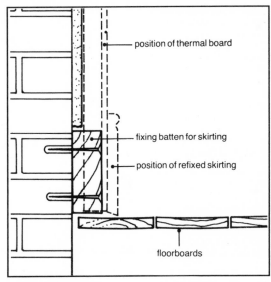

position of thermal board

fixing batten for skirting

position of refixed skirting

floorboards

3. Where there are electrical sockets or switches, first remove the appropriate fuse from the consumer unit, then the cover plate and recessed box. The box needs to be refixed on a packing piece the same thickness as the thermal board (plus about 3mm for the thickness of the adhesive), so that its front edge will be flush with the finished face of the thermal board.

Note: If the electrical wiring shows any signs of brittleness leave it well alone and call in an electrician. PVC-insulated wiring should not come into direct contact with expanded polystyrene – always sleeve the cables through short lengths of conduit. Likewise, uPVC conduit used to protect electric cables should not come into contact with expanded polystyrene.

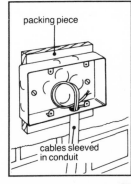

packing piece

cables sleeved in conduit

4. Mouldings to window and door openings should be carefully removed, and timber packing pieces fixed in their place. The packing pieces should be the same thickness as the thermal board, plus about 3mm for the thickness of the adhesive.

5. Window sills will have to be replaced or extended so that they project beyond the face of the new thermal board. (If you have window reveals, remove plaster to accommodate a greater thickness of insulation – see below.)

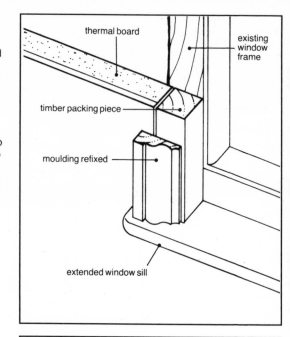

thermal board

existing window frame

timber packing piece

moulding refixed

extended window sill

6. When ordering the thermal boards always ask for ivory faced, tapered edged boards. The tapered edge makes jointing easier, and the ivory face does away with the need for a skim coat of plaster.

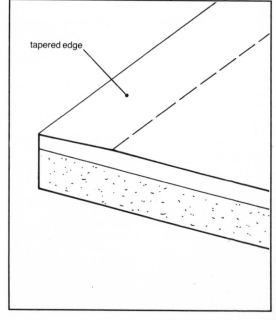

tapered edge

Fixing the thermal boards with adhesive

1. Window and door reveals should be insulated first. The thermal board at the top of the opening should be held in place for 24 hours until the adhesive is dry. The reveal boards should project from the wall by the thickness of the insulation backing.

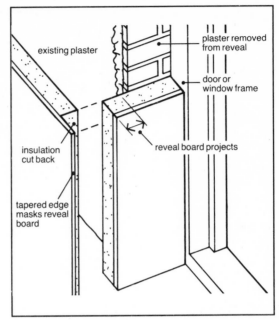

existing plaster

plaster removed from reveal

door or window frame

reveal board projects

insulation cut back

tapered edge masks reveal board

2. Mark out on the wall where the board edges occur, starting from the edge of the door or window opening. Fix one board at a time. Cut to fit between floor and ceiling, and cut out any holes for electrical sockets. Remove the insulation backing to accommodate any fixing battens and the projecting reveal board. Be careful not to damage the reveal boards.

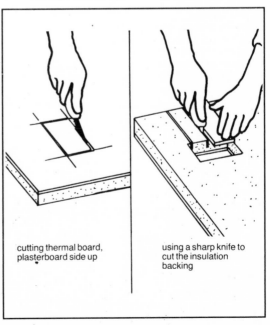

cutting thermal board, plasterboard side up

using a sharp knife to cut the insulation backing

3. Apply the adhesive to the wall in 200mm wide bands with a notched trowel as recommended by the manufacturer.
Use a length of wood to press the board firmly onto the adhesive and check that it is square and plumb. Secure the board with nine plugs and zinc-plated screws. The screw heads should be driven just below the finished surface without tearing the paper surface.

4. Joints in the plasterboard are finished by applying a thin band of filler into which is pressed the jointing tape. A second band of filler is applied to bring the joint flush with the surrounding surface.
Use a damp sponge to ensure a smooth transition between joint filler and board. Fill the recesses at the screw heads with filler. The whole surface should be covered by a slurry coat or plasterboard primer before it can be decorated.

5. Bed the skirting on sealant and screw in place. Finally refix the other timber trims that were removed, and decorate.

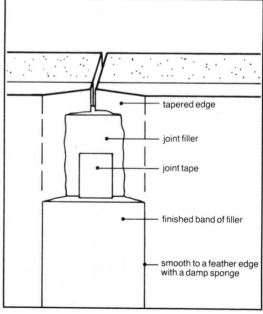

tapered edge

joint filler

joint tape

finished band of filler

smooth to a feather edge with a damp sponge

🏠 🅱 🅱

TIMBER BATTENS

This method of insulation involves screwing timber battens to the wall to form a framework for fixing plasterboard, t&g boarding or a decorative wallboard. The timber battens are infilled with insulation, usually mineral wool. You must also apply a vapour check on the warm side of the insulation, usually a 125 micron (500g) polythene sheet.

Battening out will probably be more familiar to the DIY enthusiast than fixing a thermal board, and allows the wall to be faced with t&g boarding or a decorative wallboard instead of plasterboard. This may be an important consideration if you are not confident that you can achieve a satisfactory finish from jointing and finishing plasterboard.

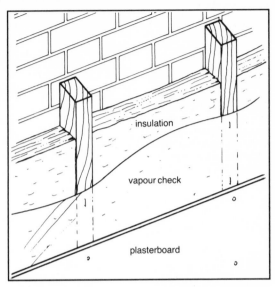

insulation

vapour check

plasterboard

Battening out is more suitable than using a thermal board where the existing plaster has lost its grip with the brickwork, or where the plaster has been removed and the brickwork is too rough and uneven for fixing a thermal board with adhesive.

Preparing to insulate the wall

1. Remove the skirting board carefully so that it can be fixed to the new wall lining and match up with the skirtings in the rest of the room. Similarly, remove mouldings to window and door frames for re-use later on.

Work out where radiators and other heavy fixtures will be going so that timber battens can be positioned accordingly.

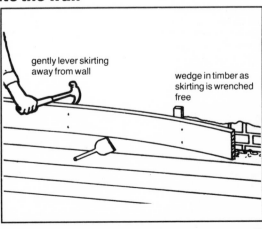

gently lever skirting away from wall

wedge in timber as skirting is wrenched free

2. Where there are electrical sockets or switches, first remove the appropriate fuse from the consumer use, then the cover plate and box. The box needs to be refixed on a packing piece so that its front edge will be flush with the new plasterboard finish.

Note: If the electrical wiring shows any sign of brittleness leave it well alone and call in an electrician.

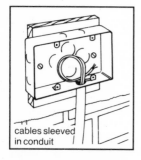

cables sleeved in conduit

3. Window sills will have to be replaced or extended so that they project beyond the new wall. Remove the plaster from window reveals to accommodate the insulation.

extended sill

4. When ordering the timber battens, ask for preservative-treated timber to prevent timber rot. Most timberyards sell pressure impregnated timber, but in a restricted range of sizes. The depth of the battens should be slightly more than the thickness of insulation, eg 65 (x 50)mm for 60mm insulation. Alternatively, you can buy a can of preservative and brush it onto untreated timber. For complete protection, the cut ends of treated timber should be given a coat of preservative, so have a small amount available when fixing the battens.

Insulating the wall

1. To ensure that the new wall lining is true and plumb you must first find the 'high spots' on the wall. To do this, mark the position of the vertical battens on the wall every 400mm. These will accommodate the 400mm wide rolls of insulation and 1.2m wide plasterboard sheets. With a timber batten and spirit level, mark the front edge of the vertical batten on the floor and ceiling. Do this for each batten, then draw a straight line on the floor and ceiling, connecting the marks *furthest* from the wall. Check in each corner that the lines are plumb.

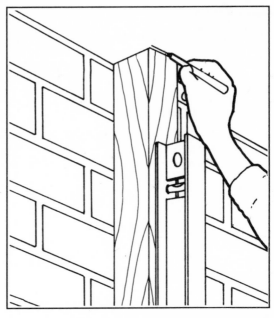

2. Fix continuous battens to the floor and ceiling so their front edges are on the lines you have drawn. Cut to length and fix the vertical battens. Screw-nail each end to the ceiling and floor battens and also provide intermediate fixings to the wall with plugs and screws. Place packing pieces behind the batten to ensure a firm framework for nailing the plasterboard. Fix extra battens for electrical sockets, radiator brackets, etc.

3. Push-fit mineral fibre between the battens. It should stay in place while the polythene vapour barrier is fixed.

Roll out the polythene sheeting on the floor and cut it square and to size. Lift it in position and staple or tack it to the battens, starting at the top. Cut small holes for electrical cables. Cut the polythene at window openings and fold it into the reveals. Keep joints to a minimum and seal all holes and joints with polythene tape.

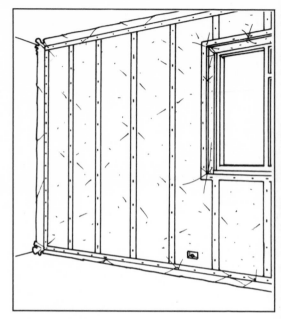

4. To avoid localised condensation on window and door reveals, these too should be insulated. Because of the limited width of window frames, it will probably not be possible to fit more than 25mm of insulation. Fix 25mm x 25mm (1in x 1in) battens as shown and fill with either expanded polystyrene or offcuts of mineral wool split down the middle to half their thickness.

The reveals are finally faced with narrow widths of plasterboard so their edges are later masked by the main sheets of plasterboard.

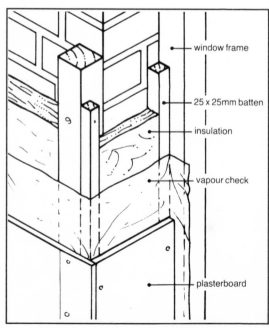

window frame

25 x 25mm batten

insulation

vapour check

plasterboard

5. Starting from one corner, begin nailing the large sheets of plasterboard to the battens. Cut the plasterboard slightly shorter than the floor to ceiling height and cut holes for electrical sockets etc. before fixing. Fix the board in contact with the ceiling, leaving a small gap at floor level. Plasterboard can be cut either by a fine-toothed saw or by scoring deeply with a sharp knife, folding it and then cutting the paper liner on the back. Use a keyhole saw for cutting holes for electrical sockets etc.

Galvanised nails should be hammered just below the surface of the plasterboard at 150mm (6in) centres.

6. Tape the joints and seal the plasterboard as described in Topic Sheet 6. Nail the skirting in place. To minimise draughts either bed the skirting on sealant or fix a draughtstrip as illustrated on page 88.

Finally, wire up the electrical fittings, and decorate.

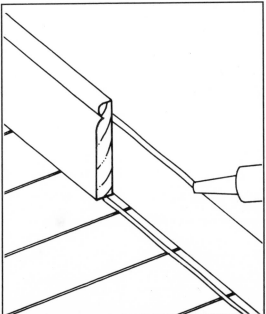

Draughtproofing is one of the most inexpensive and effective ways of making efficient use of your energy, and is within the scope of the DIY householder. A wide range of draughtproofing products are available. Choose a type made of good quality materials that suits your particular type of window or door.

The following table is based on research by the

Compression seals

Foam strip These self-adhesive draughtstrips are the cheapest available and are easy to fix. The more durable strips use PVC foam and have a

Ribbed and tubular rubber
These sections are usually made from EPDM rubber and are self-adhesive. Some tubular seals come in a holder and are nailed or screwed in place. Most of these seals need a lot of force to compress them to any great extent. Avoid painting over the

Silicone rubber tubing
This is a relatively new product. The sections are usually bedded on a bead of sealant which comes with the tubular seal in kit form. Self-adhesive sections are being introduced and should become more readily available. Silicone rubber is the most durable of the draughtproofing materials, and the thin wall of the

Wiper seals

Brush seals Self-adhesive seals are widely available, but the stiff backing can make adhesion difficult. Brush seals in an aluminium or plastic holder are more expensive but can be fixed

Fin seals A wide range of products. The cheapest are the plastic or metal spring strips. The metal strip is nailed in place and can be difficult to fit in small openings. The plastic strips are usually self adhesive. The more expensive types come in a plastic or aluminium holder. Fin seals are generally good at

Sealant

A high quality sealant similar to the sealant used around the bath. Very durable and good at filling gaps of varying width, but poor flexibility compared to other seals.
Note: Some hardwood windows are treated with preservatives and are

Building Research Establishment into the three main types of draughtproofing.

KEY	★ ★ ★	The more stars, the better
	★★★	the draught strip is likely
	★★	to perform for the window
	★	types shown
	■	Unsuitable

Window types

	Wood		Steel	
wipe-clean vinyl skin.	★★	■	■	★★
draughtstrip – paint dries very slowly over EPDM rubber and if windows are closed when the paint is still wet, they may stick tight.	★	■	■	★
tubular section readily accommodates a wide range of gaps and requires little force to compress. Can be painted over.	★★★★	★★★★	■	★★★★
to suit warped timber. Cannot be painted over.	★★	■	★★★	■
dealing with varying gap sizes, but most need a lot of effort to compress them to any great extent.	★★	■	★	■
unlikely to offer a suitable surface for sealant – most new windows are draughtproofed already.	★★★	★★★	■	★★★★

Different types of window

Vertically sliding timber windows

These are generally the most draughty type of window and also the most difficult to draughtproof. You can choose from any of the compression seals for the top and bottom of the window, but use one of the wiper seals for the sides and meeting stiles.

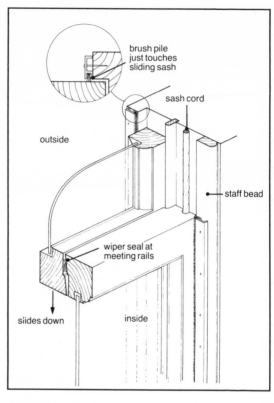

brush pile just touches sliding sash

sash cord

outside

staff bead

wiper seal at meeting rails

slides down

inside

You are likely to achieve the best results by fixing small wiper seals as shown. These are visible when the window is closed, but are probably the most effective seal for this type of window and are relatively easy to fix. Of the many wiper seals available, the brush seal is the best type as the soft nylon pile allows the sash to slide past easily. Several makes of brush seal come in plastic or aluminium holders which are pre-drilled for pinning in place. Choose a section which will look the least obtrusive.

Fix the seals when the window is closed. Measure the height of the sashes and cut the draughtstrip to length. For the upper sash fix the sections to the outside of the frame so that the brush pile just touches the sliding sash. For the lower sash fix the draughtstrip to the vertical staff bead on the inside. A less obtrusive alternative for the inner sliding sash is to fix a brush seal behind the staff bead.

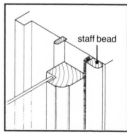

staff bead

Wooden hinged windows

If the window is not warped, and the gaps are of uniform size, adding one of the self-adhesive compression seals is the easiest solution for hinged windows.

The self-adhesive backing strips do not readily stick to dusty or greasy surfaces. To ensure good adhesion you should thoroughly clean the surfaces and allow to dry before fitting the draughtstrip. Similarly, rough and uneven surfaces should be sanded down to provide a smooth surface for the adhesive backing. It is not advisable to use wood soaked in a wax preservative because sanding down to a smooth surface will not produce a satisfactory degree of adhesion. If you are

repainting the window, wait at least a week for the paint to cure before fitting the draughtstrip.

Choose a compression seal which is suitable for the size of gap around your windows. Always fit it to the main frame, not the opening casement, and towards the inside of the frame where it is better protected from the weather.

Press the draughtstrip on to the rebated edge on the opening side of the frame as shown; on the side of the frame with the hinges it should be applied to the side of the frame.

If the fitted draughtstrip makes it difficult to close the window, you may need

to adjust the hinges or fastener. To make a small adjustment, unscrew the hinge or fastener, press a matchstick in the side of the screwhole nearest to the draughtstrip, and refix.

Where the gap size varies in width, silicone rubber tubing or a wiper seal should give better results. Silicone rubber tubing needs little force to compress the seal and is probably the best type of draughtstrip to use where gap sizes vary. Sealant can also cope with gaps of varying width, but cannot accommodate later changes in the gap size due to seasonal movement of the timber.

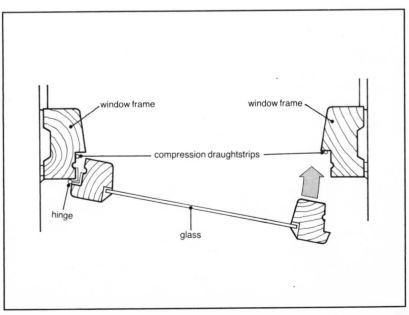

window frame

window frame

compression draughtstrips

hinge

glass

Hinged steel windows

Self-adhesive compression seals can be fitted to metal windows but the gaps are often too small and, unlike timber windows, it is not possible to adjust the hinges and catches. For small gaps the best solution is to use silicone rubber tubing or sealant. Sealant is sold in a kit form containing all you need. The sealant is squeezed onto the main window frame and a special release tape is attached to the opening frame. When the window is closed the sealant is squeezed into shape and sticks only to the main frame. After 24 hours the sealant will have cured. The release tape is removed and the excess sealant trimmed.

draughts

Doors

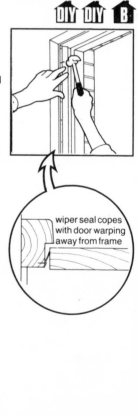

Doors are more susceptible to warping than windows, especially if they are new or where central heating has been installed. So choose draughtstrips which can accommodate some increase in gap size – silicone rubber tubing or some of the wiper seals are likely to be your best choice. Take into account that doors are more frequently used than windows, and select robust products.

The cheapest method is the sprung metal strip. This is nailed to the inside of the door rebate, starting at the top. The strip has to be cut each side of locks and hinges.

Many sections with wiper seals come in kits to suit door frames. They are fitted on the outside of the door frame. Measure the width and height of the frame and cut the draughtstrips to length.

With the door closed, screw or nail the sections in position so that the wiper blade just touches the door.

This minimises the force needed to close the door. The bottom of the door should be sealed against draughts by fixing a threshold strip. Several types are available – the most suitable for your door will depend on the design of the threshold. Threshold strips sometimes come in a variety of widths so measure your door before you go shopping.

wiper seal copes with door warping away from frame

seal just touches door

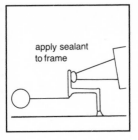

apply sealant to frame

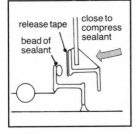

release tape
close to compress sealant
bead of sealant

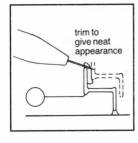

trim to give neat appearance

Automatic draught excluder
suitable for most doors

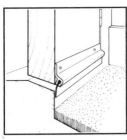

Threshold strip with wiper seal
where there is a step

drainage hole

Self-draining sill with
draughtstrip to raise the door
clear of internal floor finishes

Letter box and keyhole

DIY DIY DIY

Letterboxes can let in a lot of cold air, especially if newspapers and letters are left in all day. Covers consisting of two nylon brush seals are probably the best solution.

Some keyholes can be easily dealt with by fitting a covered escutcheon plate over the keyhole.

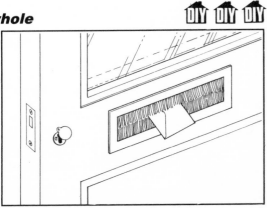

Caulking

With all windows and doors, ensure that the junction between the frame and the wall is well sealed. The existing junction may be sealed with old mortar or mastic that has cracked or fallen out. Use a non-hardening sealant which skins over or a silicone-based sealant. This allows movement to take place between the frame and wall without cracking. For uPVC window frames certain grades of neutral curing silicone sealants are especially formulated to deal with the thermal expansion encountered. Where the gaps are larger than about 6mm, you will need to push strips of polystyrene or foam rubber into the gaps as a backing for the sealant.

Draught lobbies

Adding a lobby to your front and back doors will help reduce the amount of cold air leaking into the house. Although it will only help to cut down on a very small fraction of total heat loss, it will make the house more comfortable. If the lobby is to limit the amount of cold air that enters the house each time the door is opened, it is essential that the outer door is closed before inner doors are opened or vice versa.

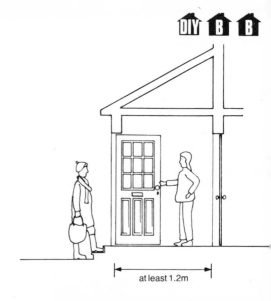

at least 1.2m

Draught lobbies can be formed by building an enclosed porch on to the outside of the house, or by enclosing part of an existing room. Try and space the doors about 1.2–1.8m (4–6 ft) apart so that there is room to let someone in from the outer door while keeping the inner door shut.

A draught lobby need not be small, but can double up as a cloakroom or a conservatory, just as long as it acts as a buffer between the main part of the house and the outside.

living room

kitchen

new entrance porch

store/lobby

enlarged lobby also serves as store for bicycles, lawn mowers etc

DOUBLE GLAZING

Installing double glazing will reduce the amount of heat lost through windows by about half. Double glazing brings other advantages too:

● **Comfort**
In winter single glazed windows create cold downdraughts when warm room air is cooled on contact with the cold glass and sinks to the floor, chilling your feet and ankles. With double glazing, the glass facing the room is warmer, so that air circulating next to it cools down more slowly, lessening the downdraught.

In cold weather, people radiate their own warmth to cold surfaces, so feel cold themselves. The warmer glass surface of double glazing reduces this chilling effect and makes the room feel warmer, without increasing the thermostat setting.

● **Window condensation**
The insulating effect of double glazing means that it has to be colder outside before condensation starts to form on the surface of the glass facing the room. (However, when a house is double glazed, problems with condensation and mould growth can occur elsewhere, such as

behind wardrobes, because background ventilation is reduced. Misting of double glazing in the kitchen or bathroom is an indication that air extraction is needed – windows should be opened or fans used.)

● **Noise**
Double glazing can reduce noise transmission through windows. The heavier the glass and the larger the gap between the two panes the better. At least 100mm (4 in) gives good results.

● **Market value**
It adds to the value of your home.

Two main types of double glazing or secondary glazing

1. Leave the existing window in place as one half of the double glazing, to which is added a second pane of glazing.

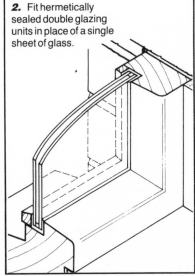

2. Fit hermetically sealed double glazing units in place of a single sheet of glass.

Hermetically sealed double glazed units

These are units made in the factory to your precise specifications, both in terms of size and the sort of glass you want, such as patterned or toughened. The hermetic seal prevents condensation occurring between the panes, but the seal is vulnerable both before fixing and during service. Careful handling and correct glazing techniques are *essential*.

When you plan to replace your single glazing with hermetically sealed units, special stepped units are available where the existing rebate is not wide enough to take the thickness of double glazing. Although more expensive than some secondary glazing systems, fitting hermetically sealed units to existing frames can be a cheap way of benefiting from their low maintenance advantages over secondary glazing systems. It has the advantage that windows open and close in the normal way.

Before ordering the stepped units, measure the windows *very* accurately and check the diagonals to make sure the frames are square. A sealed unit which does not fit will be useless unless it is only slightly too large, in which case it may be possible to trim the wooden frame. You should allow a clearance of about 4mm between glass and frame.

Also check that your frames are in good condition and that the hinges can take the extra weight – this is especially important for large opening lights. With vertically sliding windows with balancing weights you will need to buy some heavier weights. The units need to be handled very carefully to avoid damaging the seal, which will *probably* be protected by a tape. (This should not be damaged or removed.) For maximum longevity it is recommended that sealed units be 'dry-glazed' in a 'drained glazing system' – one in which the hermetic seal remains in air. Most replacement windows utilise such systems. For existing windows, however, it will usually be necessary to bed the sealed units into 'putty' much as in conventional single glazing. It is *essential* that suitable glazing compounds are used and that the sealed units are correctly supported – the latter requirement applies also to drained glazing systems.

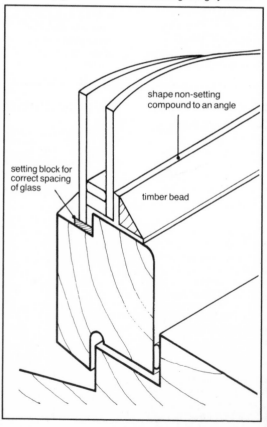

shape non-setting compound to an angle

setting block for correct spacing of glass

timber bead

In general, conventional linseed oil putty or metal casement putty must be used *only* for 'fronting' and *not* for bedding the sealed unit into the frame. Linseed oil putty should never be used for glazing flush-edged sealed units. Neither linseed oil putty nor metal casement putty should be used for glazing sealed units into timber frames which are to be treated with a microporous finish (such as a decorative exterior wood stain). Non-setting compounds – often called butyl – should be used for bedding in conjunction with setting blocks and must be of a type chemically compatible with both the hermetic seal – even if this is protected by tape – *and* the conventional putty used subsequently for fronting.

After removing the old glass and putty, paint the rebate with a sealer. Putty used for fronting should be painted in the usual way – completed within 28 days of glazing. Use of a good quality 'universal' primer overlapped approximately 2mm onto the glass (4mm in the case of stepped units), followed by gloss paint (two or three coats) will help to prevent water seeping between the putty and the glass, which is one of the causes of failure of sealed units.

The location of setting blocks and distance pieces is also important and should be at 'quarter points' for fixed lights. For side-hung windows or vertically pivoted windows different arrangements apply and the manufacturer's guidance should be followed carefully. Finally, it is important that a good seal is obtained between the butyl and the inner glass to prevent household condensation contacting the hermetic seal. An additional bead should ideally be provided and overpainted as advised for external putty.

All of the above, and the additional guidance obtainable from manufacturers, should emphasise that correct installation of sealed units is not a job for casual, uninformed DIY. Only by adhering to all technical guidance can longevity be expected from the hermetic seals. Manufacturers' warranties may be invalidated by incorrect installation. Further details are obtainable from the Glass and Glazing Federation.

If the benefits of sealed units are not particularly desired it is probably safer for DIY installers to use secondary glazing systems.

Secondary glazing

There are many types of secondary glazing, ranging from cheap plastic film to expensive, professionally installed sliding systems.

It is important to choose a system that suits your windows. Fixed (non-opening) systems need to be taken down and stored in summer to allow ventilation. The more expensive DIY systems and professionally installed secondary glazing are hinged or slide so that windows can be opened for ventilation throughout the year. Do not seal windows so that they cannot be opened: windows are a valuable escape route in the event of fire.

Plastic films

These are the cheapest and easiest way of double glazing, but are not intended to be permanent. The cheapest films are only intended for one heating season, while the thicker films will probably need taking down each time windows are decorated.

DIY fixed glazing

There are a number of fixed pane systems designed for the DIY market which use glass or sheets of rigid plastic. The simplest methods use magnetic strips or Velcro tape to hold the glazing in position. You must use plastic glazing with these two methods. They are easy to remove in an emergency and for cleaning. Other methods have a channel that is secured by screw fixings or clipped in position and is less easy to remove in a hurry.

It is preferable to glaze opening windows separately by fixing the secondary glazing to the frames of opening lights. Make sure that window catches and fasteners can operate when the secondary pane is in position.

Magnetic strip secondary glazing

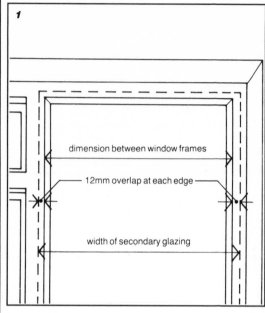

dimension between window frames

12mm overlap at each edge

width of secondary glazing

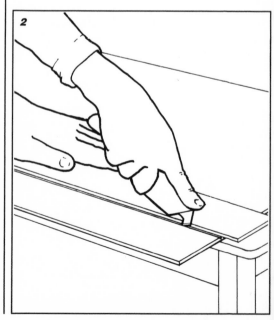

1. Magnetic strip consists of a steel strip with a self-adhesive backing which is fitted to the frame, and a magnetic strip or channel which is fitted to the secondary glazing. Measure the window. One large sheet can be fixed across the whole window, or the opening lights treated separately. Buy the plastic glazing, allowing 12mm overlap at each edge.

If possible, fit the glazing on a cold, dry day. Clean the inside of the window and the frame and allow to dry.

2. Cut the glazing to size. You will need a sharp knife, with a blade designed for cutting melamine sheet, and a straight edge. Score the cut line several times and then snap the sheet over the edge of a table. Check the cut sheet against the window and use a pencil to mark its perimeter on the frame.

3. With a small hacksaw cut the metal strip to length. Peel off the backing tape and press the strip onto the window frame, just inside the pencil line.

4. Cut the magnetic strip or channel to size and fix to the plastic glazing. Lift the glazing into position.

Hinged and sliding secondary glazing

These are the most expensive types of secondary glazing. Most are designed to be installed within the window recess and are the most suitable type of secondary glazing where noise reduction is important. For maximum noise reduction the gap between the existing window and the secondary glazing should be at least 100mm (4in).

The frames are made of aluminium or plastic and incorporate draughtproofing. The secondary frames can be opened for ventilation and cleaning.

Most systems come in kit form, often in height and width packs for home assembly and installation. Some firms offer to make up secondary windows to your measurements, cutting the frames to size and fitting the glazing, ready for you to fix.

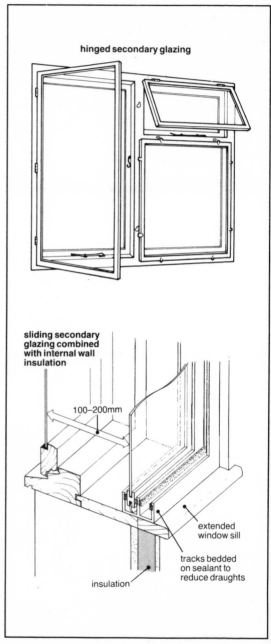

hinged secondary glazing

sliding secondary glazing combined with internal wall insulation

100–200mm

extended window sill

tracks bedded on sealant to reduce draughts

insulation

Condensation

If the seal around the secondary glazing is not effective, warm room air will seep into the space between the two panes and cool. As it cools, condensation may form on the cold outside pane. If this is a problem ventilate the cavity to the outside with 6mm (1/4in) holes, about every 600mm (24in), through the window frame. Loosely pack the holes with glass fibre to trap insects.

Safety

If you install secondary glazing, make sure you can escape by the window in an emergency – a fire, for example. Remember that plastic glazing is very difficult to break and, if you use glass, you may have to attack it at its edge with a sharp object (eg the back of a panel hammer) and make a hole large enough to escape through without cutting yourself.

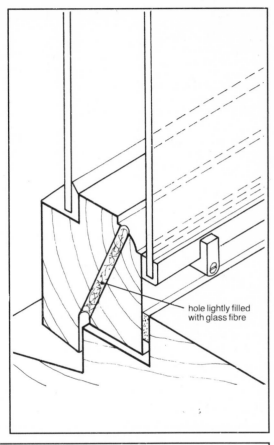

hole lightly filled with glass fibre

Dealing with replacement window salesmen

Your builder should be capable of installing replacement wood or steel windows, but for other materials you may need to call in a specialist firm. This will involve inviting sales representatives into your home. They can be persuasive and try to make you sign on the spot, so:

- get prices from at least three firms

- don't sign anything immediately, and say that you are awaiting quotes from other firms before coming to a decision

- don't be rushed by offers of discounts or warnings about imminent price increases

- ask to be given the address of previous jobs in your area so you can check on their delivery times and workmanship

- see also box on page 83 about a consumer protection plan

Insulating shutters

For those who are serious about energy conservation, insulating shutters are the most effective way of reducing heat loss through windows. They cannot be bought in the shops, but the simpler types are not a difficult DIY job.

The main consideration is how to fit the shutters, and how to remove and store them during the day to let in the daylight.

At the simplest level, removable panels can be made to fit within the window reveals as shown. The main drawback is in storing the panels during the day. Hinged or sliding panels overcome this problem, but are difficult to use in conjunction with curtains. For wide windows, several panels can be made to fold aside like a concertina.

The larger the window the more difficult it is to find an acceptable method of accommodating the shutters. Shutters can be faced with wallpaper or fabric to match the interior decor, or be made a feature by facing with posters, prints or a decorative roller blind material.

If condensation arises special drainage channels can be inserted in the frame to carry water away.

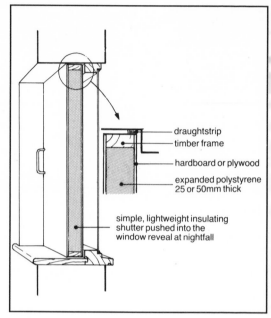

draughtstrip
timber frame
hardboard or plywood
expanded polystyrene 25 or 50mm thick

simple, lightweight insulating shutter pushed into the window reveal at nightfall

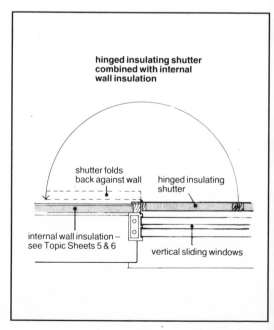

hinged insulating shutter combined with internal wall insulation

shutter folds back against wall

hinged insulating shutter

internal wall insulation – see Topic Sheets 5 & 6

vertical sliding windows

Replacement windows

If your windows are in a poor condition, you might consider having replacement windows installed.

The main factors which most affect your choice of window are likely to be price, appearance and future maintenance. Whatever type of window you decide on, look out for these features:

● **Double glazing**
Replacement windows should always be double glazed. The extra cost will soon pay for itself in energy savings, increased house value and in other ways.

● **Good quality built-in draughtproofing**
Aluminium and PVC windows already come with a good standard of draughtproofing, but an increasing number of manufacturers are making timber and steel windows with built-in draughtproofing.

● **Trickle ventilation**
Each room should have a means of controlling ventilation – see overleaf for how important this is. Ask your supplier how trickle ventilation is provided – it may be an optional extra.

● **Condensation removal**
In kitchens and bathrooms ensure that condensation problems are solved first by installing an extract fan.

● **Thermal break**
If your present windows suffer from condensation, any new aluminium or steel double glazed windows are also likely to suffer from condensation on the frame unless they incorporate a thermal break.

Windows with any of these features will cost more than windows without them, but they will make your home more comfortable and should help to keep your heating costs down.

Glass and Glazing Federation's consumer protection plan

If your double glazing is installed by a member of the Glass and Glazing Federation you will benefit from the Federation's Code of Practice and Deposit Indemnity Scheme. These are explained in a video: for details write to the Federation at the address on page 111.

Replacement doors

Most people select a replacement door because of its appearance rather than its insulation value. However, good-looking, highly insulated doors are now available, complete with frame, threshold and draughtproofing that works like a fridge door. You may prefer to fit one of these doors rather than build a draught lobby.

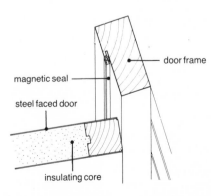

door frame

magnetic seal

steel faced door

insulating core

CONTROLLABLE VENTILATION

Draughtproofing windows and doors and sealing other gaps and cracks will cut out excessive ventilation responsible for uncomfortable cold draughts. However, it is important to ensure that there is provision for finely controlled ventilation. One method of doing this is by the use of trickle ventilators which are designed and fitted into the head of the window frame.

Trickle ventilators are sometimes incorporated in some replacement windows or may be offered as an optional extra. They are not widely available and you may have to search them out at an architectural ironmongers. Plastic vents are usually shorter and cheaper; aluminium vents are available in a range of lengths – some are cord-operated, which is essential where you cannot reach the window head.

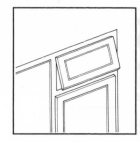

If your window incorporates a small top vent, this can be used in the same way as a trickle ventilator albeit without the same fine degree of ventilation control.

Fitting a trickle ventilator

The correct size of the ventilator depends on the size of the room. A rule of thumb is that the ventilator should be 50mm (2in) long for each 1m^2 of floor area. So a room of 12m^2 would need a 600mm (24in) long ventilator, or two small 300mm (12in) long ventilators.

Mark out the position of the ventilator on the window head. Make sure the window section is deep enough to accommodate the ventilator.

Drill a series of holes of the size required (usually 12mm or 16mm diameter) in a straight line. Clean up the hole with a chisel to form a continuous slot to the length required.

On the outside fit the part of the vent with the fly screen. On the inside fit the controllable part of the vent. Make sure you cover over the slot.

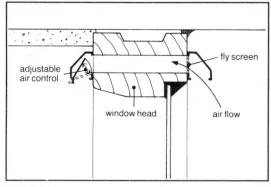

adjustable air control

fly screen

window head

air flow

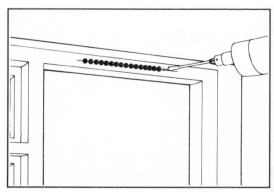

Alternative methods of trickle ventilation

If the section of your window head is not suitable for fitting a
trickle ventilator, there are three main alternatives.

Trickle ventilator in the glazing

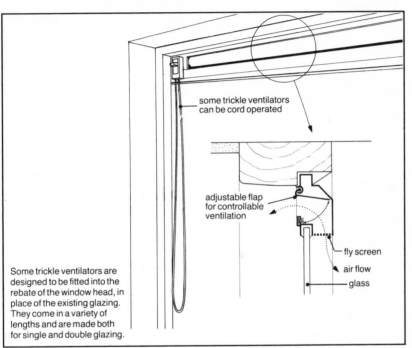

some trickle ventilators
can be cord operated

adjustable flap
for controllable
ventilation

fly screen

air flow

glass

Some trickle ventilators are
designed to be fitted into the
rebate of the window head, in
place of the existing glazing.
They come in a variety of
lengths and are made both
for single and double glazing.

Night vent fastener

If you have side hung
windows, you can replace
your ordinary window catch
with a *night vent fastener*.
This allows you to keep the
window slightly open whilst
maintaining security. Some
makes are available which
can be locked in position.
Night vents are easy to fix,
but offer less variable
control than trickle
ventilators.

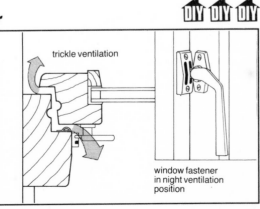

trickle ventilation

window fastener
in night ventilation
position

Hit and miss ventilator to chimney flue

Many older houses have an unused flue to each main room which can be used to provide controllable ventilation. The ventilators should ideally be fitted at high level and be of the *hit and miss* type (that is, the ventilator can be either open or shut). These are widely available. Sweep the chimney before you knock out the hole.

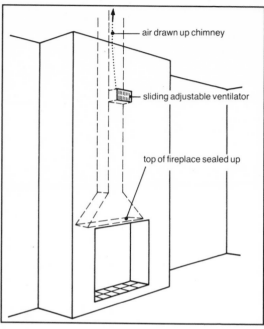

air drawn up chimney

sliding adjustable ventilator

top of fireplace sealed up

Caution

If you have a gas or coal fire which discharges into a flue, be very careful that you break into an unused flue. If you are in any doubt, seek professional advice.

Kitchens and bathrooms

The ventilation of kitchens and bathrooms may need special attention because of the amount of moisture generated there.

Moisture generated in the kitchen and bathroom tends to disperse throughout the house and will condense on the coldest surfaces – usually the windows. Unless your home is well insulated and heated, condensation may also form on other cold spots such as walls (particularly in exposed corners and unheated bedrooms), window reveals and concrete floors, and may eventually lead to mould growth.

One of the best ways of removing excessive moisture at source is to install an extract fan. A kitchen extract fan has the added advantage that it also removes cooking smells.

Extract fans can be fitted in a number of ways:
- in the glass of a window
- built into an outside wall
- as part of a cooker hood
- fixed to the wall or ceiling with a duct to the outside
- fans operated by temperature differences.

Caution

If you fit an extract fan in a room with an open fire or a non-balanced flue boiler, you should also provide permanent ventilation, such as an airbrick, to ensure a supply of air for combustion.

When the rest of your house is well insulated, the heat loss through the timber ground floor can account for a significant proportion of your heat loss. In addition, feet and ankles are particularly sensitive to cold and draughts, and a warm floor is a considerable asset. The heat loss through ground floors occurs in two ways:

- cold draughts percolate through the gaps and cracks in the floor. This is a particular problem in older houses with square-edged floorboards

- heat is lost by conduction through the thin floorboards – this can be reduced by insulation. Laying a carpet and underlay or cork tiles also helps a little.

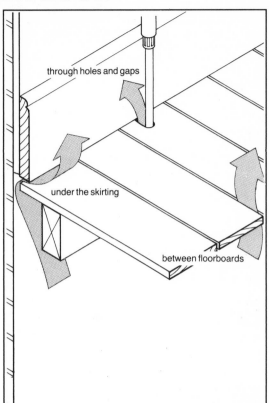

through holes and gaps

under the skirting

between floorboards

Dealing with draughts

Cutting down on draughts should be your first priority. There are three main areas where draughts percolate through the floor.

1. Between the floorboards. Draughts between floorboards are generally only a problem in houses built before about 1920 which have square-edged floorboards. Floorboards in later houses

have tongue and grooved joints which give a much better seal. Laying hardboard over the whole floor will eliminate draughts between the boards. Where you are laying a thin sheet or tiled floor finish, you will need to lay hardboard or thin plywood over your floorboards to provide a suitable laying surface. Laying carpet paper or building paper

under fitted carpets should be almost as effective, and cheaper.

Before laying, hardboard should be wet slightly on the textured side, using 2 pints of water for a 2.4m x 1.2m sheet, and stacked flat for 48 hours. This will prevent ripples forming in the sheet if it absorbs atmospheric moisture in the future. The sheets should be laid in a staggered pattern and nailed to the floor every 200mm around the edge, and about every 400mm across the centre of the sheet, where the joists occur. Use hardboard pins about 20mm long.

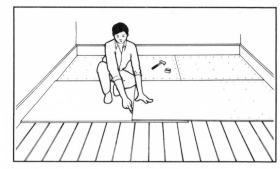

2. Gap under the skirting boards. There are two ways of dealing with this. Either fill the gap with a sealant or cover with a timber bead.

Choose a sealant that does not just skin over but fully cures, such as an acrylic emulsion type. Otherwise the surface skin may be broken when carpets are laid and that could be very messy. Always vacuum clean to remove loose dirt and dust before applying the sealant.

Timber beads should be pinned to the floor. This allows for later movement as the skirting board expands and contracts or if the floor sinks. If the floorboards are uneven it may be necessary to bed the timber bead on a thin bead of sealant to take up the undulations.

If you are fixing new floorboards or refixing old ones, add a draughtstrip to the bottom of the skirting before nailing it in position.

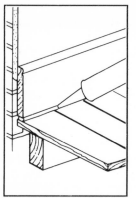

Sealant applied from a cartridge

Draughtstrip fixed to skirting before refixing

Timber bead bedded on sealant and pinned to the floorboards

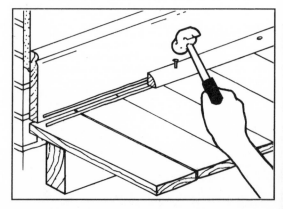

3. Gaps and holes in the floor where pipes, wires and cables rise from below should be sealed. Small gaps can be sealed with silicone sealant. For larger holes, foamed polyurethane is now

available in aerosol cans and is ideal for filling awkwardly shaped gaps and holes, but it is expensive. An alternative is to cover the hole with an offcut of vinyl flooring or something similar.

Carefully cut the vinyl about 25mm (1in) wider than the hole to fit tightly around the pipe. Use a sealant to bed the offcut to the floorboards and to seal any remaining gap around the pipe.

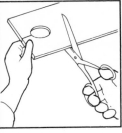

Cut out template to cover hole

Apply sealant around hole

Press template into position and seal around pipe

Points to consider

● The ventilation **below** a suspended timber floor **must** be maintained to prevent timber rot and mould growth. So uncover blocked ventilation grilles and ensure that they do not become obstructed by the level of your path being raised for example, or by accumulated rubble and spiders' webs.

● If you are adding central heating to your house for the first time, the wood will gradually dry out and shrink over the first one or two heating seasons. This will create more gaps and cracks for draughts and will be particularly pronounced where new wood has been used – for skirtings and floorboards for example. So check after a year that the draughtproofing of floors is still effective.

● It may be wise not to draughtproof straight away in a new house where new furniture has been installed and building work recently carried out. Draughtproofing may be easier when all timber has settled down.

Adding insulation

Adding insulation to your suspended timber floor will be worthwhile provided it can be carried out easily. So, if you have a cellar or need to take up large numbers of floorboards to carry out repair work, the cost of adding insulation should soon be recovered in savings on your heating bill. If your modernisation work does not entail taking up your floorboards, the cost of taking up the floor just to lay insulation is unlikely to be cost-effective, unless you do the work yourself. Two ways of insulating a timber floor are shown on the following pages.

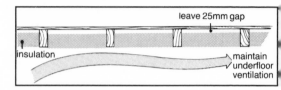

Fixing insulation from below

There are two main ways of insulating a timber floor from below:

Method 1
Insulation quilt is pushed up between the joists and held in place by plastic netting.

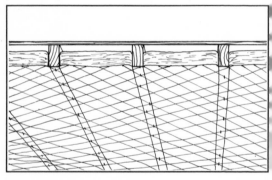

Method 2
Rigid insulation boards are friction-fitted between the floor joists. Expanded polystyrene is the most suitable insulation material.

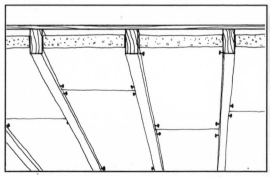

Method 1 — insulating quilt 🏠 🏠 🅱

Push ordinary loft insulation quilt between the joists. Wear a mask, goggles and gloves when handling the quilt as loose fibre can cause irritation. In many older houses where the floor joists are spaced at less than 400mm (16in) centres the insulation quilt may be held in place by friction. Where the insulation needs support, staple thin garden netting (most garden centres sell a lightweight mesh for protecting fruit cages or as a clematis support) to the underside of the floor joists.

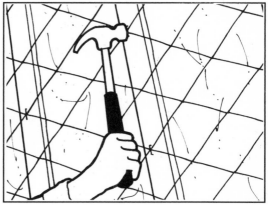

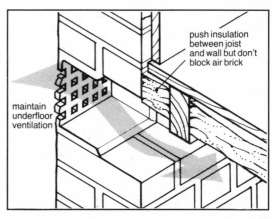

push insulation between joist and wall but don't block air brick

maintain underfloor ventilation

Method 2 — rigid insulation board

Sheets of expanded polystyrene are available in 25mm (1in) and 50mm (2in) thickness in sizes from 4' x 2' to 8' x 4'. The only tools you need are a knife or fine-toothed saw to cut the polystyrene, a tape measure and a hammer.

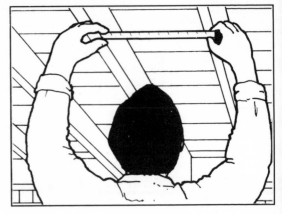

Measure the width of the joists and cut the polystyrene 2–3mm wider than the joist spacings. Simply push the insulation in place. If cut to the correct size the insulation should hold itself in place by friction. If it is a loose fit, hammer in some large headed nails (such as plasterboard nails) to keep the insulation in place. Butt joint adjacent boards as you work along. Carefully work out how to cut the large sheets of insulation to minimise wastage. Leave a gap of about 25mm (1in) between the insulation and the underside of the floorboards.

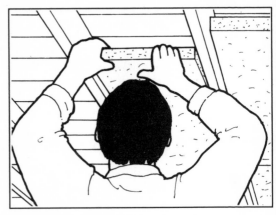

Caution

Keep electrical cables below the insulation. Where cables pass through the insulation, they should be protected from contact with the polystyrene by short lengths of protective channelling.

Fitting insulation from above DIY B B

The two methods for fixing insulation from below can be adapted for fitting insulation from above the floor. One of the problems with fitting insulation from above is that floorboards are usually continuous underneath partitions. This means that it is not always possible to achieve ready access to all parts of the floor and some 'Heath Robinson' ingenuity may be needed at times.

Method 1

To fix the support netting it is necessary to drape the netting over the joists and staple it to the sides of the joists as shown. The netting should hang loose enough to support the insulation quilt and leave a 25mm (1in) air gap above it.

Method 1 – insulating quilt

Method 2

To ensure that the polystyrene insulation is not shaken loose when the floorboards are nailed back, the insulation boards should be supported on plasterboard nails, hammered in to half their length to the sides of the joists. Use four nails to each insulation board. For 50mm (2in) thick insulation boards, position the nails 75mm (3in) below the top of the joists to leave a gap of 25mm (1in) above the insulation.

Method 2 – rigid insulation board

Central heating and water pipes should run above floor insulation where possible. Even central heating pipes above the insulation should be insulated – if they are left bare, the heat will warp the floorboards directly above them, and you may end up with creaking floorboards.

While the floorboards are up, check that there are no obstructions to the underfloor ventilation. Have a good look at the condition of timber members, especially the wall plates and where joists are built into the wall.

Upper floors

In most houses it is only the ground floors that need insulating. Only where upper floors are exposed to outside air on their underside should they be insulated. This may occur where your house has a recessed entrance porch or a passage to provide access between front and back gardens. Most floors in these situations are of timber construction and are readily insulated. Floors of rooms over integral garages should also be insulated.

Take up a couple of floorboards along each side of the area to be insulated. Cut lengths of loft insulation quilt to size and gently push the insulation between the joists. Carefully pull the insulation through the floor void and tuck it against any outside wall so there are no cold spots.

Any gaps and cracks in the soffit should be sealed to prevent draughts.

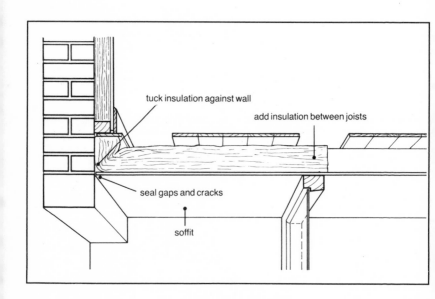

tuck insulation against wall

add insulation between joists

seal gaps and cracks

soffit

TOPIC 12 — INSULATING A CONCRETE FLOOR

Unless you are laying a new concrete floor or relaying a screed, the opportunities for insulating a solid floor are very limited.

Laying a floor finish that is warm to the touch, such as carpet or cork tiles, helps to overcome the cold feel of a concrete floor but provides very little insulation. Where you want to lay a thin floor finish, such as sheet vinyl or cork tiles, but the existing concrete surface is too rough to lay the flooring direct, consider laying a 'floating' floor.

A floating floor consists of a layer of insulation overlaid with hardboard or chipboard to give a smooth, firm surface for the new floor finish. It is called 'floating' because the hardboard or chipboard is not nailed or fixed to the original floor, but just rests on top. A floating floor can also be used in place of laying a new sand/cement screed, and because it uses dry materials it does not have to dry out, but is immediately ready to receive any floor finish. This can speed up improvement work.

Laying a floating floor
Before you start work

The first thing to check is whether the old concrete floor suffers from rising damp. You can test for dampness by taping a piece of clear polythene sheet to the floor. If the floor suffers from dampness, within 2–3 days drops of water will start to form on the underside of the polythene, and you will need to lay a damp proof membrane (DPM) before you lay the floating floor.

The DPM can either be polythene sheet (250 microns, 1000 gauge) or a brush-applied bitumen solution. The new DPM should lap with the damp proof course in the wall to provide complete protection from rising damp.

The thickness of insulation should be chosen so that the finished floor is level with any adjoining floor. If this is not possible, the step should be not more than about 40mm (1 in). This height of step can usually be accommodated at a door opening. Avoid raising the floor level in a hallway with stairs as the change in height to the last step may make the stairs dangerous.

Use flooring grade chipboard which usually comes in sheets 2.4m x 0.6m with tongue and grooved edges. In kitchens and bathrooms or where water is likely to be spilt you must use a moisture resistant chipboard (should be type 11/111 to British Standard 5669), sometimes called V313 chipboard and tinted green.

1. Remove the skirting boards and unscrew any doors that open into the room. Lay boards of expanded polystyrene, closely butting the joints between the boards. Polystyrene is available in 13mm (1/2in), 25mm (1in) and 50mm (2in) thicknesses. Next lay a sheet of polythene over the insulation to act as a vapour barrier. Turn the polythene up the wall and fix it up behind the skirting.

95

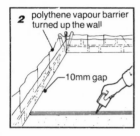

2. Lay the chipboard, leaving a 10mm gap around the perimeter for expansion. The tongue and grooved joints should be glued and adjacent sheets tightly fitted together. Joins in the chipboard should not coincide with joins in the insulation.

3. Re-fix the skirting. You may have to cut the bottom off any inward opening doors before rehanging them to ensure that they clear the new floor finish. With external doors you may have to fit a new threshold to deal with the raised floor level – see Topic Sheet 8.

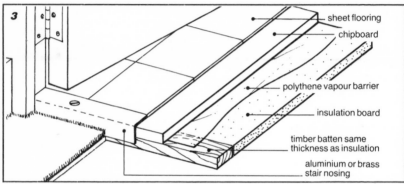

sheet flooring

chipboard

polythene vapour barrier

insulation board

timber batten same thickness as insulation

aluminium or brass stair nosing

Insulating a new concrete floor

You may be laying a concrete floor in a new extension, or be replacing an old timber floor that has extensive timber rot. Whatever the reason, you should include insulation in the new floor. The cost of doing this is little more than the cost of the material, but the cost of adding insulation at some future date would be prohibitive. The opportunity to insulate the floor will probably never occur again.

Floor insulation is of greatest benefit in rooms with two or more outside walls. This is because solid floors lose a large proportion of their heat through the edges of the floor next to the outside walls. So if you are building a new extension with two or more outside walls, floor insulation makes a lot of sense.

There is a choice of two positions for the insulation:

Under the slab

This is the better option where the new floor is in a south-facing room. The large mass of concrete can be used to absorb heat from the sun's rays during the day, and acts like a large low temperature radiator during the evening. The insulation should be rigid and resistant to moisture. High density expanded polystyrene is the most commonly used material. A special extruded type of polystyrene combines high strength and minimum water absorption and is particularly suited for use below the damp proof membrane.

The whole floor area should be covered. The slabs should be butt jointed and the joints taped with a water resistant tape. Strips of insulation should be placed around the perimeter of each room as shown – this prevents heat loss through the edge of the slab. The concrete floor is then laid in the usual way, care being taken not to damage the insulation.

Above the slab

This is the better choice for basements and north-facing rooms which do not benefit from plenty of sun. Placing the insulation above the concrete means that the floor surface warms up quickly when the heating is switched on.

The construction is the same as for the floating floor described earlier except that the insulation is usually 50mm thick. The concrete slab should be finished off fairly evenly as a base for the DPM and rigid insulation board.

With a new concrete floor it should be possible for the new floor level to match up with the existing floor, without the need for a step. Moisture resistant chipboard should always be used in kitchens, bathrooms and wherever water is likely to be spilt. Alternatively, sand/cement screeds are commonly used.

It is preferable to place the DPM above the slab so that there are no problems of moisture from the newly laid concrete slab drying out and damaging newly laid floor finishes. Because the insulation and chipboard are dry materials, they can be walked on immediately after laying and are ready to receive any floor finish. In contrast, sand/cement screeds can take several weeks to dry out completely.

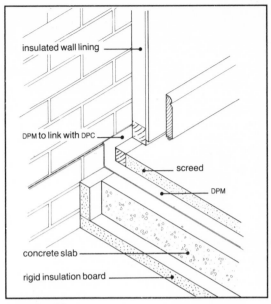

Under the slab

Above the slab

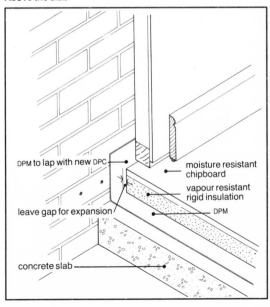

No matter how well you insulate and draughtproof your home, if your heating system cannot sense when temperatures are high enough it will not switch itself off, but continue supplying heat which you don't need. Whatever form of heating you have or are planning to install, the cost of keeping rooms at a comfortable temperature and providing adequate hot water can be kept down if you are able to control your heating system properly.

Deciding on a heating system

Most people installing a new heating system choose a conventional central heating system with radiators, so this Topic Sheet deals primarily with controls for this type of heating. We also describe the latest developments in the design of central heating boilers. But in a well-insulated home central heating is not necessarily the best answer, especially for smaller homes, where individual heaters are likely to provide sufficient heat and be cheaper to install. So on the next few pages we describe controls for individual room and water heaters.

Controlling a central heating system

All modern central heating boilers have their own boiler thermostat to control the temperature of the water that leaves the boiler. Unless switched off, the boiler and pump continue to send water around the heating system, heated to the temperature set by the boiler thermostat, regardless of how hot the house and hot water become.

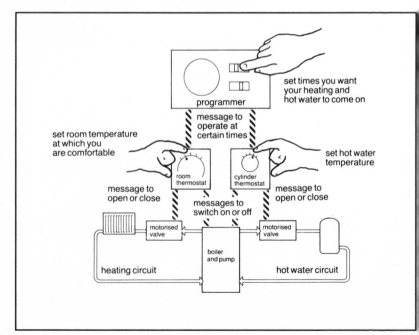

set times you want your heating and hot water to come on

programmer

message to operate at certain times

set room temperature at which you are comfortable

room thermostat

cylinder thermostat

set hot water temperature

message to open or close

messages to switch on or off

message to open or close

motorised valve

motorised valve

boiler and pump

heating circuit

hot water circuit

To switch off the boiler and pump when the house temperature is comfortable and the hot water reaches the desired temperature you need two types of thermostat: one to sense the air temperature in the house (a *room thermostat* or *thermostatic radiator valve*), the other to sense the temperature of the hot water in the hot water cylinder (a *cylinder thermostat*).

To enable independent control of the heating and hot water, you need motorised valves. These are opened and closed by signals from the thermostats. Finally, to switch the heating and hot water on and off at the times you want, you need a *programmer*.

These controls are described in more detail below.

Room thermostat

The most common type of thermostat for a central heating system is a room thermostat fixed to the wall. The thermostat keeps the temperature steady by turning the heat on and off automatically. Once the room with the room thermostat reaches the set temperature, the heating throughout the house is switched off.

For this reason the thermostat should be put in the most frequently used room, probably the living room, unless there is a thermostatic radiator valve there. Position it away from

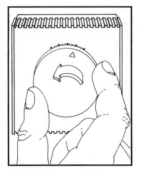

draughts and direct sunlight and ensure it is not hidden by curtains or affected by heat from table lamps or the television, for example.

Although the living room is probably the best place for the thermostat, if it contains another heat source such as a coal or gas fire, the best compromise may be to put the room thermostat in a non-draughty position in the hall.

How to use thermostats

Experiment with the thermostat setting until you find the lowest temperature at which you are comfortable. Many people find 18°C (65°F) adequate while they are moving about the house. Those who are less active, such as the elderly and very young children, usually need 21°C (70°F). Unless your house is well insulated, you may find that you need to turn your thermostat up in very cold spells to counteract the cold radiation from windows and walls. But don't forget to turn it down again as the weather gets warmer. Every 1°C (1.5°F) increase in the room thermostat setting increases fuel consumption by about 10 per cent.

Thermostatic radiator valves

These replace the normal hand valves on radiators. A thermostatic radiator valve (TRV) works by reducing the flow of water to its radiator as the thermostat reaches its set temperature. Fitting valves to an existing system is a plumbing job that may involve draining down the whole system.

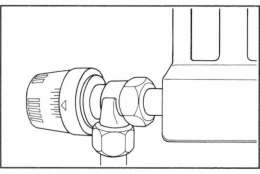

TRVs give good temperature control in individual rooms, automatically compensating for both internal and external influences on room temperatures. They can be fitted to every radiator and in any case should be fitted in those rooms which are most likely to overheat (kitchens and sunny bedrooms). They should also be fitted where you frequently wish to change temperature settings for short periods (bathrooms and study bedrooms) and where you require only background heating most of the time (unused bedrooms).

As there is usually no electrical connection they cannot switch off the boiler and pump when the demand for heat has been satisfied; they are therefore best used in conjunction with a room and cylinder thermostat control system (they must not be fitted to radiators in the same room as a room thermostat), or by one of the newer types of boiler control devices which turn off boiler and pump when the demand for heat has been satisfied.

Cylinder thermostat

Most central heating systems also heat the hot water cylinder. Providing it is not a solid fuel boiler, you can ensure more economic operation of your hot water system by fitting a clamp-on cylinder thermostat linked to a motorised valve or a non-electric thermostatic valve. Setting the thermostat at, say, 55°C (130°F) will prevent the water from the hot taps becoming scalding hot or risking scale-formation in the cylinder.

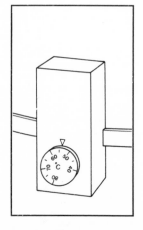

Programmer

A programmer is a time switch for your central heating that turns the heating and hot water on and off automatically at the times you set. It is easily adjustable as the seasons vary and saves you money because it gives you heat only when you want it.

It also adds to your comfort because you can set it to switch on while you are out and have a warm house when you return. Allow for the time the house may take to warm up and cool down by setting the time clock to go on and off half an hour early. Don't be afraid to change the time switch on warm winter days or when you are going away, to achieve the longest 'off' periods consistent with comfort.

If you have room and cylinder thermostats and motorised valves, you will be able to programme your heating and hot water separately. Here's how a programmer works.

In the example illustrated (yours is likely to be different but the operating principles will be similar), the central heating (CH) can be set to four positions:

- on 24 hours

- on once (usually on in the morning and off again in the evening)

- on twice (on and off for a period in the morning, on in the afternoon and off again in the evening)

- off.

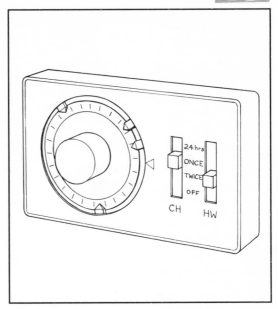

The hot water system (HW) can be set likewise, to any one of four positions.

Most programmers have indicator lights to show you at a glance what is on.

Once the controls have been set the way you want them, the time clock will turn the heating and hot water on and off as required. For example, you can set your hot water on continuously, but your heating for two periods during the day or in the summer you can set the programmer to give you hot water morning and evening, but with no heating.

The benefits of a programmer are considerable; if you use it, it will enable you:

- to have hot water when you want it in the morning, without the inconvenience of having to get up early to switch on or the expense of leaving it on all night

- to come home in the afternoon to a warm house without the extravagance of leaving the heating on all day

- to save money by minimising the risk of forgetting to turn off when you go out, or when you go to bed.

To benefit from the greatest economy, experiment with the time intervals and with the programme settings to give you just what you want. To do that, you'll need to change your settings, particularly when the weather becomes warmer in spring.

Radiators

A simple, cheap and effective way of increasing the efficiency of radiators on outside walls is to stick reflective aluminium foil to the wall behind. This reflects heat back into the room that would otherwise be lost through the outside wall. Ordinary aluminium cooking foil can be used, but several proprietary brands tend to be easier to install.

Fitting a narrow shelf above a radiator will help to deflect heat into the room that would otherwise rise up to the ceiling. This will be of most benefit if you have high ceilings or where radiators are located under windows. Fit a draughtstrip to the back of the shelf to

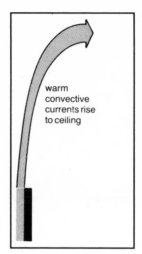

warm convective currents rise to ceiling

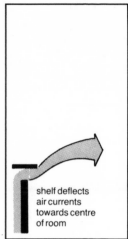

shelf deflects air currents towards centre of room

eliminate any gaps with the wall – hot air rising through narrow gaps can cause unsightly pattern staining.

Do *not* hang curtains over radiators as much of their heat will be lost out of the window.

A new heating system

Make sure your heating installer takes your insulation and draughtproofing improvements into account when sizing a new heating system – this should save you money because you need smaller radiators and boiler.

If your improvement work includes installing a new central heating system the following features and controls should ensure efficient and economical operation:

● a low thermal capacity boiler made of lightweight cast-iron or aluminium, or a copper tubing system

● a fully pumped system – pumping water through both heating and hot water circuits (these are available for solid fuel appliances now)

● a programmer

● a room thermostat with a motorised valve controlling the heating circuit

● thermostatic radiator valves in intermittently used rooms such as the kitchen, bathroom and bedrooms

● a cylinder thermostat with a motorised valve controlling the hot water circuit; sometimes a single motorised valve can control both heating and hot water

● both thermostats wired up to control the boiler and pump.

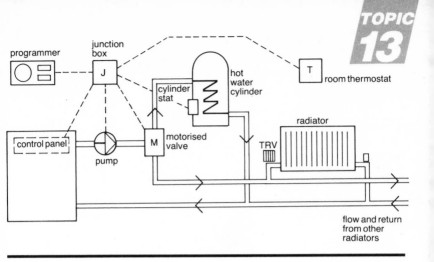

Improving an existing central heating system

Most central heating boilers are much more efficient than those produced 10 years or more ago. The replacement of a 10–15-year-old boiler and the installation of modern controls may reduce fuel costs by up to 35 per cent. Most older central heating systems only have simple controls. The hot water circuit will not be pumped, but usually works by gravity.

Such a system relies entirely on the householder switching it on and off by hand and adjusting the boiler thermostat to compensate for changes in the weather. If you want the advantages of automatic controls, you need to add a programmer, room thermostat, cylinder thermostat and motorised or non-electric thermostatic valve. Ask your heating contractor how easy it would be to change the pipework so that the pump also serves the hot water circuit.

Developments in boiler design

Over the past few years a great deal of research aimed at improving the efficiency of central heating boilers has emerged. Today's gas and oil boilers of apparently 'conventional' design use much less fuel to produce the same amount of heat than those manufactured over 10 years ago. The fruits of this research are two significant new types of gas boiler, the combination boiler and the condensing boiler. New developments in oil fired and solid fuel boilers are also at an advanced stage and new boiler designs should appear in the showrooms over the next few years.

New solid fuel boilers which are highly automated and can burn house coal smokelessly and efficiently are available now.

The combination boiler

These gas appliances combine the function of a central heating boiler and hot water cylinder in a single unit. Models are now available up to 80,000 Btu (British thermal units).

Combination boilers are very compact and are designed to fit either under the kitchen worktop or in an airing cupboard. Wall-hung models are also available.

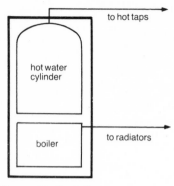

The combination boiler

The condensing boiler

This is the latest development in the design of gas boilers. A condensing boiler is the most efficient type of boiler available and, unlike the conventional gas boiler, its efficiency remains high even when working at low level output. The seasonal efficiency of a condensing boiler is around 85 per cent compared to around 70 per cent for a new conventional gas boiler. This increase in performance is achieved by extracting more heat from the waste flue gases by allowing them to condense in the boiler. This means that as well as the usual connections to gas and cold water supplies, a condensing boiler also needs a drainage connection. The higher cost of the boiler together with the extra cost of a drainage connection mean that a condensing boiler is most suitable for a medium-sized or large house where the extra installation costs will be more quickly offset by savings on the gas bills.

Other heating and hot water controls

As an alternative to central heating you may prefer to install individual heaters. For a well-insulated house individual heaters will almost certainly work out cheaper to install and can be just as economic and convenient to use.

You may prefer to control your heating manually, in which case there is a wide range of heating appliances to choose from. However, an increasing number of appliances are now available with some degree of automatic control, and we describe these below.

Electric storage heaters

A storage heater works by storing heat at night when electricity is available at the cheap off-peak rate. The heat is released into the room during the following day and evening. Modern storage heaters have two controls. The input control is set to adjust the amount of heat stored overnight – the colder the weather the higher the setting. The second control regulates the rate at which heat is released into the room. The degree of control is limited, especially by evening when much of the stored heat will have been released.

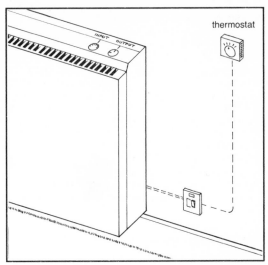

To ensure a comfortable temperature without overheating it is necessary to adjust the input control to anticipate the following day's weather. Some storage heaters have their own thermostat which does this job for you. The thermostat is either built-in or wall-mounted. It measures the room temperature as the heater is being charged and controls the amount of heat being stored. Alternatively, you can control several storage heaters in a similar way with an outside thermostat. Ask at your electricity board showroom for details about the latest controls.

Gas fires and convector heaters

The majority of gas fires and convectors are controlled manually, but some models incorporate thermostats, and a few of these can be controlled by a time clock. Ask your local gas board for details. More efficient condensing room-heaters are likely to appear in the showrooms over the next year or two and may be worth considering (see condensing boilers opposite).

Water heating by immersion heater

Heating your water with Economy 7 off-peak electricity will help keep your running costs down. To make the best use of off-peak electricity your hot water cylinder should be well insulated and the heating controlled by a time clock.

A new off-peak system consists of a well-insulated hot water cylinder with two immersion heaters and a time control. The lower immersion heater is wired up to come on a pre-set number of hours to heat the water at night, using off-peak electricity. The upper immersion heater uses full-price electricity and is wired up to a one-hour timer on the time control. This allows you to top up the hot water for up to an hour if necessary.

Each immersion heater has its own thermostat to control the temperature of the hot water. Set the lower thermostat at about 60°C (140°F), and the upper thermostat a little lower.

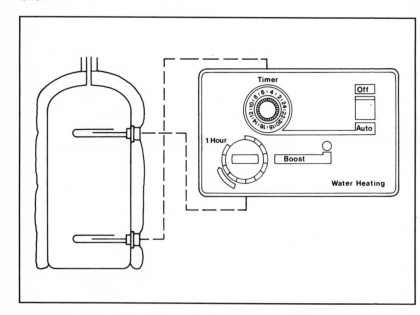

Water heating by gas

Independent gas water heating can be by means of an instantaneous water heater or a gas circulator serving a hot water cylinder. Both appliances have their own internal thermostats and once set up are designed to operate automatically, providing hot water on tap as required.

Choosing a builder

The ideal builder should be cheap, quick, well organised and have workers who are tidy, reliable and produce good quality work. A pin in the yellow pages is unlikely to find your ideal builder first time.

Personal recommendation or local knowledge are the best ways of selecting a list of builders to tender. If a builder has done good work for someone you know, the chances are he will also do a reasonable job for you.

The staff at your local council who administer the Building Regulations and Improvement Grants may be able to give you a list of builders they know who do home improvement work. However, they can't officially recommend an individual builder.

Failing satisfactory recommendation, three organisations are prepared to supply lists of member firms in your area:

- The Federation of Master Builders
  Gordon Fisher House
  33 John Street
  London WC1N 2BB
  Tel: 01-242 7583

  (Warranty scheme – details from the Registrar, National Register of Warranted Builders, at the above address)

- Building Employers Confederation
  (formerly the National Federation of Building Trades Employers)
  82 New Cavendish Street
  London W1M 8AD
  Tel: 01-580 5588

  (Guarantee scheme – details from:
  BEC Building Trust Limited
  Invicta House, London Road
  Maidstone, Kent ME16 8JH)

- Scottish Building Employers Federation
  13 Woodside Crescent
  Glasgow G3 7UP
  Tel: 041-332 7144

Before adding a builder to your list, always ask for a list of recently completed jobs. This will allow you to see the quality and scope of previous work, and obtain the views of the people who have had the work done.

When you do find a builder who looks good remember that a number of other people may have come to the same conclusion, and you may find you will have to wait some time before work can start.

The following checklist is issued by the Office of Fair Trading for people who are thinking of having work done to their home.

Before you start
Decide exactly what you want done. For larger jobs, consider getting advice from an architect or surveyor.

Council approval
Ask your local authority whether you need planning permission or building regulations approval and whether you can get a grant towards the work.

Shop around
Don't be rushed. Get estimates or quotations in writing from at least three firms. Find out as much as you can about the firm. Can it cope with the job? If in doubt, get a second opinion.

Your contract
Make sure your contract is in writing and gives full details of prices, cancellation rights, guarantees and when the work will be started and finished. Check whether any subcontractors are to be used and who is liable if things go wrong.

Payment
Be careful about parting with money in advance especially if you are asked to pay large deposits. Always query any price increases and ask why they were not included in the original estimate.

If you have a problem
Act quickly and get advice from your local Trading Standards (or Consumer Protection) Department, Citizens Advice Bureau or Consumer Advice Centre.

(From the Office of Fair Trading's booklet *Home improvements* which sets out your legal rights and gives advice on avoiding common pitfalls when having your home improved)

Glossary

balanced flue
A type of flue which combines the combustion air inlet and the flue outlet used on some gas fired boilers and water heaters. A balanced flue appliance does not need a separate supply of combustion air

butt joint
A joint where two pieces of flat material meet at their edges without overlapping

DPC or damp proof course
A layer of impervious material laid in a wall (usually about 150mm above ground level) to prevent rising damp. A chemical DPC is injected into the wall

DPM or damp proof membrane
A layer of impervious material laid or painted on a concrete floor to exclude groundwater from the building

hermetic seal
The airtight seal between two panes of a factory-made double glazing unit

motorised valve
A valve in a central heating system which controls the flow of water. The valve is opened or closed by means of a small electric motor

rendering
A layer of sand and cement mixture usually applied to the outside of walls – often finished with a pebbledash or paint finish

reveal
The internal side surface of a window or door opening

sarking felt
A lightweight felt laid under roof tiles or slates

screed
A layer of sand and cement mixture, usually about 50mm (2in) thick, laid on a concrete floor to provide a smooth, level surface for the flooring finish

skim coat
The finishing coat of plaster about 3mm (1/8in) thick applied to a plastered wall

slurry coat
A runny cement/water mixture

soffit
The surface forming the underside of overhanging eaves or a projecting floor

spalling
Where the outside surfaces of concrete or brickwork crumbles or flakes away – usually as a result of frost damage

t&g boarding
(or tongue and grooved boarding) Timber boarding where the tongue in one board fits the groove of its neighbour

thermal barrier
The insulating material that separates the inner and outer sections of a steel or aluminium window frame

trickle ventilator
A small, manually controlled ventilator, usually located in the head of a window frame

uf foam
A foam used to insulate cavity walls (see page 52)

vapour check and vapour barrier
A layer of airtight materials which prevents warm moist air in a building passing into and condensing within a wall or roof (see page 14)

SOURCES OF FURTHER INFORMATION

Further help and advice on how to save energy in the home
may be obtained by contacting:

- Your local British Gas or Electricity Board showroom.
  In many of the larger showrooms there are specialist energy advice centres where staff can demonstrate and give advice on energy savings

- Your local Domestic Coal, Electricity or Gas Consumers Council

- Your local office of the Solid Fuel Advisory Service or Living Fire Centre – call (0783) 673578 for the address of your nearest contact

- Your Oil supplier

- Liquefied Petroleum Gas Industry Technical Association, 17 Grosvenor Crescent, London SW1X 7ES. Tel: 01-245 9511

- Paraffin Heating Advisory Council, 121 Gloucester Place, London W1H 5FB. Tel: 01-935 8164

- The Builders' Merchants Federation, 15 Soho Square, London W1V 5FB. Tel: 01-439 1753

- Home Heating Link Line: Heating and Ventilating Contractors Association, 34 Palace Court, London W2 4JG. Tel: (0345) 581158 (for names of contractors to provide impartial advice on heating systems)

- National Association of Plumbing, Heating & Mechanical Services Contractors, 6 Gate Street, London WC2A 3HX. Tel: 01-405 2678

- Scottish & Northern Ireland Plumbing Employers Federation, 2 Walker Street, Edinburgh EH3 7LB. Tel: 031-225 2255

- Building Centres in Birmingham, Bristol, Durham, London, Manchester and Paisley (for information on materials, controls, appliances and suppliers)

- Builders' merchants and BMF-approved Heating Display Centres

- Energy Efficiency Office, Department of Energy, Thames House South, Millbank, London SW1P 4QJ

- Heat Pump Manufacturers Association, 2nd Floor, Nicholson House, High Street, Maidenhead, Berkshire SL6 1LF. Tel: (0628) 34667

  (See your local telephone directory for addresses and telephone numbers as necessary)

Loft insulation

Eurisol – UK Mineral Wool Association, St Paul's House, Edison Road, Bromley, Kent BR2 0EP. Tel: 01-466 6719

National Association of Loft Insulation Contractors (NALIC) PO Box 12, Haslemere, Surrey GU27 3AN. Tel: Haslemere (0428) 54011

Hot water cylinder jackets

Insulating Jacket Manufacturers Federation, Ideal Insulation (Burton) Ltd, Little Burton West, Derby Street, Burton-on-Trent, Staffs DE14 1PR. Tel: Burton-on-Trent (0283) 63815

Cavity wall insulation

British Board of Agrément, PO Box 195, Bucknalls Lane, Garston, Watford WD2 7NG. Tel: Garston (0923) 670844 Hotline for checking on or obtaining list of approved firms: (0923) 662900

National Cavity Insulation Association, PO Box 12, Haslemere, Surrey GU27 3AN. Tel: Haslemere (0428) 54011

Eurisol–UK Mineral Wool Association, St Paul's House, Edison Road, Bromley, Kent BR2 OEP. Tel: 01-466 6719

Expanded Polystyrene Cavity Insulation Association, 5 Belgrave Square, London SW1X 8PH. Tel: 01-235 9483

The Cavity Foam Bureau, P.O. Box 79, Oldbury, Warley, West Midlands B69 4PW. Tel: 021-544 4949

Draughtproofing

Draughtproofing Advisory Association Limited, PO Box 12, Haslemere, Surrey GU27 3AN. Tel: Haslemere (0428) 54011

Solid wall insulation

External Wall Insulation Association, PO Box 12, Haslemere, Surrey GU27 3AN. Tel: Haslemere (0428) 54011

Heating and Energy Saving Centre, The Building Centre, 26 Store Street, London WC1E 7BT. Tel: 01-637 1022 (Permanent exhibitions, seminars, visitors welcome)

Double glazing

Glass and Glazing Federation, 44–48 Borough High Street, London SE1 1XP. Tel: 01-403 7177

Controls

Hevac Control Manufacturers Association, Nicholson House, High Street, Maidenhead, Berks SL6 1LF. Tel: (0628) 34667

Financing your home improvements

The best ways to finance your home improvements are:

- with cash or from savings
- through an extension to your mortgage
- through a bank loan.

If you do not have sufficient cash or savings, you should ask your building society (or bank) to finance the improvements through an extension to your mortgage. A mortgagee will usually be very willing to consider this, particularly for the more expensive measures. For other measures the best method may well be a loan from your bank.

Other Government publications

Energy efficient renovation of houses – a design guide
A publication equivalent to this book for building professionals, available from HMSO

Cutting home energy costs – a step-by-step Monergy guide available from the Energy Efficiency Office – see page 110.

Other publications from Which?

The Which? Book of Home Improvements and Extensions
A comprehensive, practical guide full of ideas and advice on the subject – a key to a new home without the expense of moving

The Which? Book of Do-it-Yourself
A fully illustrated book for all home-owners, from the most inexperienced to the accomplished DIY enthusiast

The Which? Book of Plumbing and Central Heating
A handbook for all householders who would like to carry out the majority of plumbing jobs in their home

Details of these three books and others published by Consumers' Association can be obtained from:
Consumers' Association, Castlemead, Gascoyne Way, Hertford SG14 1LH.